Matthew Mohan-Hick

Matthew Mohan-Hick

THE
GEOGRAPHY
OF THE EARTH

THE
GEOGRAPHY
OF THE EARTH

Sue Brooks

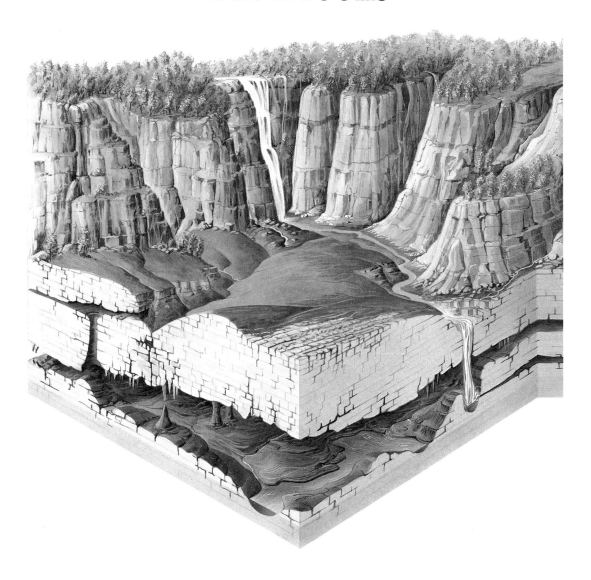

Horus Editions

Designed by Paul Richards (Designers and Partners)

Illustrated by John Downes, Mike Saunders, David Wright, Janos Marffy, Brian Pearce
(Kathy Jakeman Illustration), Gary Hincks, Robert Morton (Bernard Thornton Artists),
Ron Hayward (Hayward Art Group).

Edited by Elizabeth Miles

CIP catalogue record for this book is available from the British Library

ISBN 1-899762-04-3

Copyright © 1991 Ilex Publishers Limited
This edition Copyright © 1995 Horus Editions Limited

First published 1995
Second impression 1996

Published by Horus Editions Limited,
27 Longford Street, London NW1 3DZ

Printed in Singapore

CONTENTS

THE EARTH MACHINE

I T IS not known how the Earth first came into existence, but scientists have been able to explain some of the early stages in its making. From around 4500 million years ago, planet Earth became hotter and hotter, fuelled by chemical changes in its rocky interior. The centre of the Earth was melted by these heat-generating chemical reactions, but the surface remained much cooler. This heat difference caused convection currents to develop in the molten mantle, allowing it to circulate, stirring and mixing the Earth's materials. Over hundreds of millions of years the light materials became separated from the heavy particles, creating the layered Earth we live on today. All around the Earth we find evidence that it is still not a static, unchanging mass, but that it is highly dynamic.

Inside the Earth

As the Earth was forming, heavy materials in the Earth sank towards the centre, to become what we call the core. The light material floated to the surface, to form a thin, solid crust of rock. This is separated from the core by a thick, semi-molten mantle of denser rock. Heat from the centre of the Earth causes the mantle to circulate, rising to the surface in some places, before spreading out, cooling and sinking. The crust now floats on the mantle, like a raft on the sea. It is 100 kilometres thick, and thinner under the oceans than under the continents. Since the Earth is almost 6400 kilometres in diameter, the crust is only a thin skin-like covering. It acts as a great insulating jacket, keeping heat inside the Earth, but remaining cool enough at the surface to allow life to exist.

NORTH AMERICA

MID-ATLANTIC RIDGE

SOUTH AMERICA

CRUST

UPPER MANTLE

LOWER MANTLE

OUTER CORE

INNER CORE

OCEAN

CONTINENT

Convection currents in the mantle move pieces of the crust, or plates, from place to place.

Dynamic Earth

Where the crust's plates collide, rocks are crumpled and folded, forming mountains. Often one plate rides over the other, especially where an oceanic plate meets a continental plate. Then the oceanic plate dips beneath the continental plate, entering the interior of the Earth where the rocks melt. All along the Atlantic Ocean is a long, winding ridge made up of huge sub-sea mountains, many higher than Mount Everest. Here the American plate is moving away from the European and African plates, causing the escape of molten material from the mantle and the formation of these oceanic volcanic mountains.

The moving plates

The thin skin of the Earth, called the crust, is divided into a series of separate plates. Floating on the mantle, they can move slowly from place to place. They move in different directions, sometimes parting from each other and in other places colliding. They can also slide past each other, causing tremors and earthquakes. Tectonics, or plate movements, have a huge effect on the Earth.

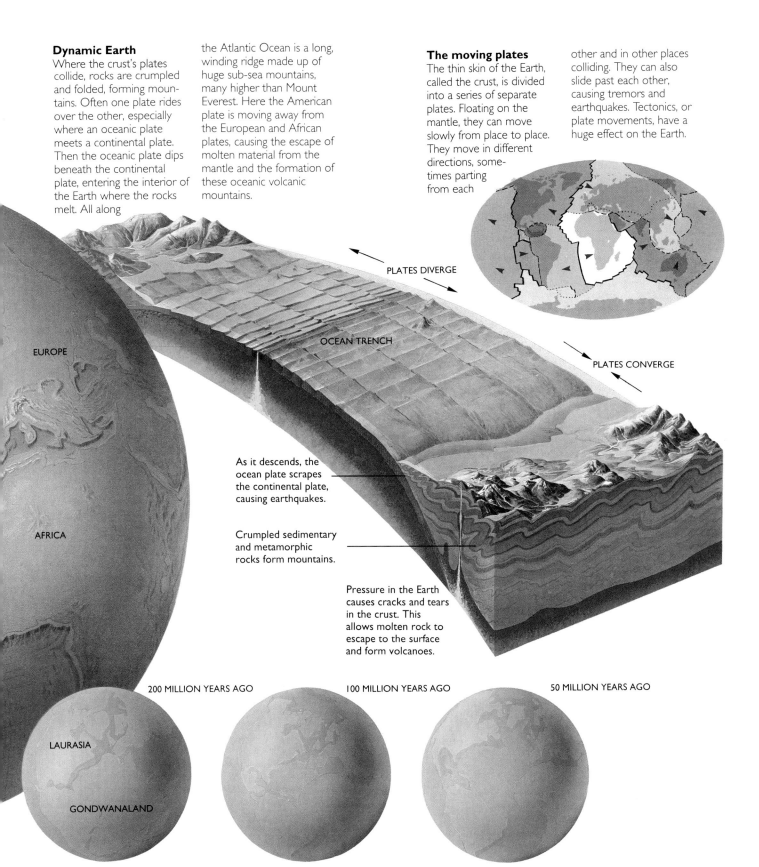

EUROPE

AFRICA

PLATES DIVERGE

OCEAN TRENCH

PLATES CONVERGE

As it descends, the ocean plate scrapes the continental plate, causing earthquakes.

Crumpled sedimentary and metamorphic rocks form mountains.

Pressure in the Earth causes cracks and tears in the crust. This allows molten rock to escape to the surface and form volcanoes.

200 MILLION YEARS AGO

100 MILLION YEARS AGO

50 MILLION YEARS AGO

LAURASIA

GONDWANALAND

Changing continents

Around 500 million years ago, the continents were all assembled as a giant supercontinent, known as Pangaea. This continent initially split into two, Gondwanaland and Laurasia, and later into the several smaller continents we see today. It is thought that Europe was once joined to North America and that these continents split apart 120 million years ago. Since then, the plates carrying these continents have been drifting further away from each other, and the Atlantic Ocean has been growing bigger. Fifty million years ago the arrangement of the continents was beginning to look more as it does today.

The air around us contains water as an invisible gas, called water vapour. The amount of water vapour in the atmosphere determines its humidity. Regions which are very humid, such as tropical rainforests, have a lot of water vapour in the air. Deserts, on the other hand, are surrounded by air with very little water vapour. Evaporation from the surface of rivers, lakes and the sea supplies the atmosphere with water vapour. Hot air can hold a lot more water vapour than cold air, and at night when the air cools, it cannot carry all it has taken up during the day. The water vapour condenses to form droplets, seen as dew or frost on the ground early in the morning.

Water cycle

PRESSURE differences over the Earth's surface cause air to move from place to place, and water vapour is taken along with it. If the air is forced to rise, such as when it has to pass over a mountain, it cools down. The invisible water vapour condenses around tiny specks of dust or salt to form visible droplets of water, which can be seen as clouds.

Eventually the droplets become too heavy for the air to support them and the water falls to the ground as snow, rain or hail. The water then runs down slopes to rivers in which it travels to the sea. As the sea water heats up under the sun, it evaporates and the whole

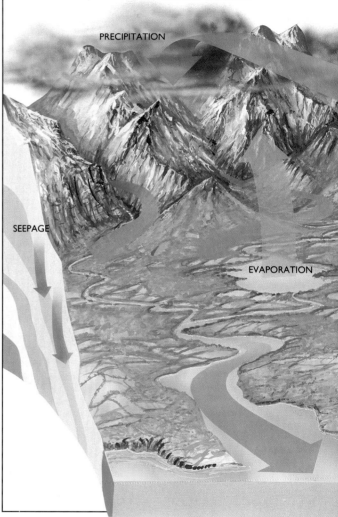

PRECIPITATION

SEEPAGE

EVAPORATION

Thunderstorms

The most spectacular storms are due to intense heating of the ground, and a transfer of the heat to the air. Molecules in the air begin to move around very rapidly when the air is heated. Their movement causes the air to expand. In doing so it becomes much lighter, rising to great heights and developing towering clouds with large drops of water. The cloud base develops a strong negative electrical charge, while the Earth's surface and cloud top have a positive charge. Sparks, seen as lightning, are generated by this difference in electrical charges, and as the energy is discharged, a shock wave travels through the air which can be heard as thunder.

View from a satellite

A satellite image of a thunderstorm shows the spiralling pattern of swirling, towering clouds. The edge of the storm is very abrupt; the rain could flood one area, while leaving nearby areas completely dry.

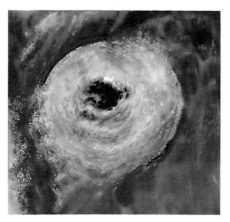

Global winds

Differences in temperature over the Earth cause the atmosphere to circulate, moving heat from the equator to the poles. Hot air rises at the equator because of great heating of the ground, and then spreads towards the poles. The oceans also warm up and flow away from the equator, moving heat towards the poles.

cycle begins again. In this way, water molecules are moved round and round, passing between the atmosphere and the land, and back again.

As water or ice travels across the land it gradually erodes the landscape, helping to change the scenery of the Earth.

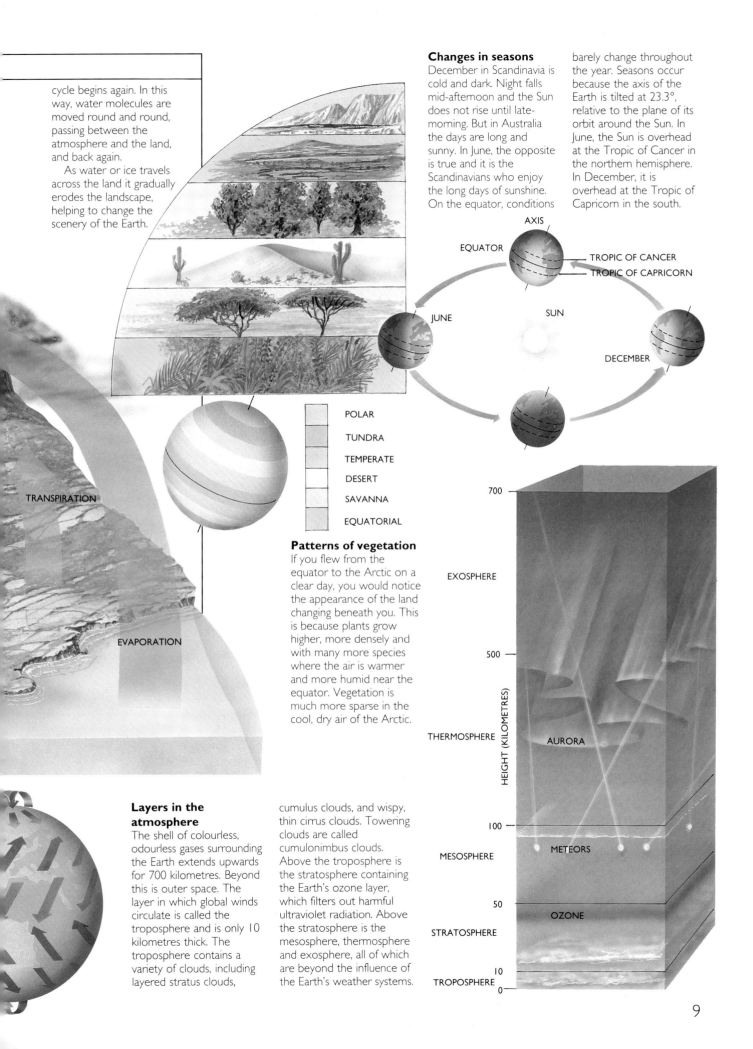

TRANSPIRATION

EVAPORATION

POLAR
TUNDRA
TEMPERATE
DESERT
SAVANNA
EQUATORIAL

Patterns of vegetation

If you flew from the equator to the Arctic on a clear day, you would notice the appearance of the land changing beneath you. This is because plants grow higher, more densely and with many more species where the air is warmer and more humid near the equator. Vegetation is much more sparse in the cool, dry air of the Arctic.

Changes in seasons

December in Scandinavia is cold and dark. Night falls mid-afternoon and the Sun does not rise until late-morning. But in Australia the days are long and sunny. In June, the opposite is true and it is the Scandinavians who enjoy the long days of sunshine. On the equator, conditions barely change throughout the year. Seasons occur because the axis of the Earth is tilted at 23.3°, relative to the plane of its orbit around the Sun. In June, the Sun is overhead at the Tropic of Cancer in the northern hemisphere. In December, it is overhead at the Tropic of Capricorn in the south.

AXIS
EQUATOR
TROPIC OF CANCER
TROPIC OF CAPRICORN
JUNE
SUN
DECEMBER

700

EXOSPHERE

500

THERMOSPHERE

AURORA

HEIGHT (KILOMETRES)

100

MESOSPHERE

METEORS

50

OZONE

STRATOSPHERE

10

TROPOSPHERE

0

Layers in the atmosphere

The shell of colourless, odourless gases surrounding the Earth extends upwards for 700 kilometres. Beyond this is outer space. The layer in which global winds circulate is called the troposphere and is only 10 kilometres thick. The troposphere contains a variety of clouds, including layered stratus clouds, cumulus clouds, and wispy, thin cirrus clouds. Towering clouds are called cumulonimbus clouds. Above the troposphere is the stratosphere containing the Earth's ozone layer, which filters out harmful ultraviolet radiation. Above the stratosphere is the mesosphere, thermosphere and exosphere, all of which are beyond the influence of the Earth's weather systems.

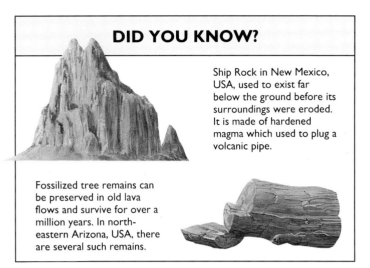
Rock cycle

THE cycle of rocks around the globe is driven by ice, wind and water. Over millions of years these agents of erosion can cause the land surface to be lowered by thousands of metres, unless movements in the Earth's crust lift the land back to its previous height. Glaciers, formed from ice, are pulled by gravity towards the sea, pulverizing the rock beneath them as they go. In areas too warm for glaciers, water makes its way to the sea in channels (rivers), carving valleys into the landscape. In arid regions, such as deserts, wind also erodes the rock. All these powerful agents pick up and transport small fragments of rock, as well as soil particles. In some cases chemical processes dissolve the rock which is then carried to the sea as a solution. Deposited in the sea as sediment, some of the rock and soil particles will eventually be uplifted to begin the cycle again.

Volcanoes

The formation of primary rocks at the Earth's surface is often accompanied by huge blasts of power in a volcanic explosion. Molten magma shoots to the surface, along with a cocktail of ash, cinders and harmful gases. The magma at the surface, called lava, solidifies as it runs across the land. In this way, the volcano is built up layer by layer with each eruption. Ropy lava can sometimes form if the surface of the flowing lava cools to form a skin, whilst molten rock continues to flow beneath.

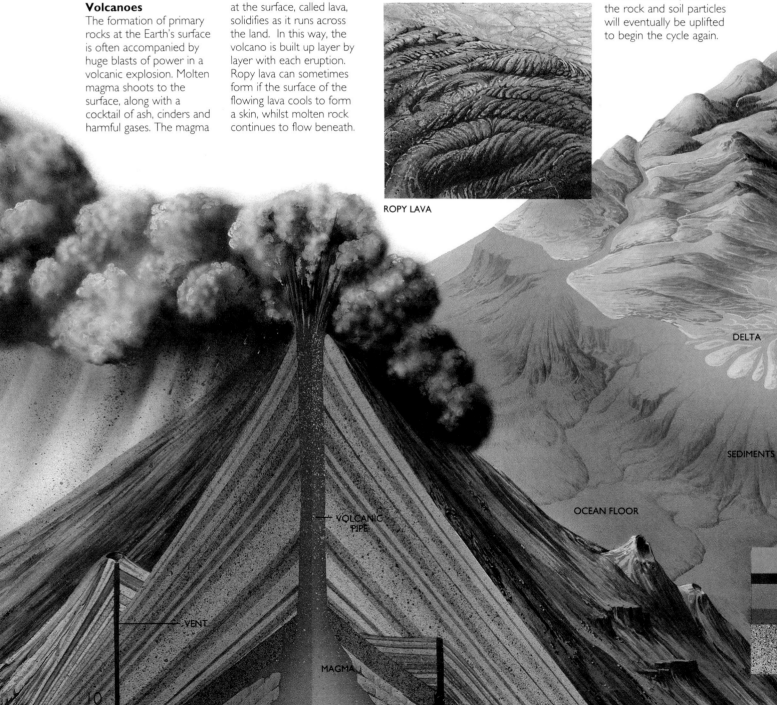

ROPY LAVA

DELTA

SEDIMENTS

OCEAN FLOOR

VOLCANIC PIPE

VENT

MAGMA

Marble

Beautifully coloured marble is widely used as a decorative building stone. It is a metamorphic rock formed from limestone which has been changed by intense heat and pressure.

Sedimentary rocks

THE sedimentary rocks are so-called because they are composed of sediments which collect in a deep basin, or geosyncline, on the sea floor. Also added to the sediment are the skeletons of marine creatures. The sediments form layers which differ according to their composition. Through time, coarse-grained sediments form sandstones and fine-grained particles form shales. Sedimentary layers alter as the environment changes, and so they can become a useful record of past conditions on land. Tectonic movement lifts the layers, exposing them to renewed erosion.

VALLEY

RIVER

The Earth's oldest rocks are almost 4 thousand million years old. The first rocks, or primary rocks, were igneous rocks formed from cooling magma from the interior of the Earth. Rocks such as granite and basalt are igneous rocks, containing many different minerals. Because they are composed of different combinations of the 2000 minerals in existence, they are varied in appearance and in their resistance to erosion by water, wind and ice. Secondary rocks, otherwise known as sedimentary rocks, are formed from igneous primary rocks. A third group of rocks, the metamorphic or tertiary rocks, form from both primary and secondary rocks when they are changed by intense heat or pressure.

Rifts and nappes

If rocks are displaced along a fault so that one side is lower than the other, the process is called rifting (below, left). A nappe occurs if the rock is folded, sliced off at the base, and moved for great distances (below, right).

Carboniferous forest

MOST of the world's coal is from forests of the Carboniferous Period, around 300 million years ago. The coal formed from the remains of old vegetation which, as it died and decomposed, accumulated during past geological periods. As more sediments were piled on top, the weight changed the material to coal.

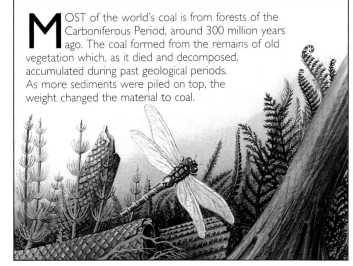

A fish on land

Mudskippers are actually fish, but they feed and mate on dry land. They have adapted to life both in and out of the water, and have a special skin which can absorb oxygen, but only if it is kept moist. They move across the muddy plains in mangroves by slowly crawling along on their front fins, although occasionally they shoot across the mud by flicking their tails.

MUDSKIPPER

Life on Earth is organized into an intricate series of food chains and food webs, where food is passed from one organism to the next. All life relies on tiny organisms which live in the soil and take nitrogen from the air so that it can be used by plants. As they grow, plants change basic mineral substances to simple sugar or food molecules which nourish plant-eating animals called herbivores. Herbivores in turn are eaten by carnivores. After plants and animals die, minerals are returned to the soil to be recycled.

Adapting to life

SOME habitats are so difficult to live in, plants and animals have to be specially adapted to survive. Fennec foxes have unusually large ears, which help to keep them cool in the extreme heat of the desert. Plants like the spiky naras melon cope with extreme dryness by developing very long roots which reach water deep in the ground.

SPIKY NARAS GRASS

Life in the soil

Soil dwellers vary according to the climate and rock in the area. In temperate regions the largest creatures include moles which burrow through the soil, eating worms as they go. Smaller creatures include centipedes which eat microscopic insects such as mites.

Soils

Soils are a mixture of rock particles from the earth and organic matter from decayed plants. Near the surface there is more organic matter, but deeper in the soil there are only broken fragments of rock.

Soil dwellers (right)
1) Millipede 2) centipede 3) earthworm 4) termite

5) beetle 6) sawfly
7) caterpillar
8) microorganisms.

Life on Earth

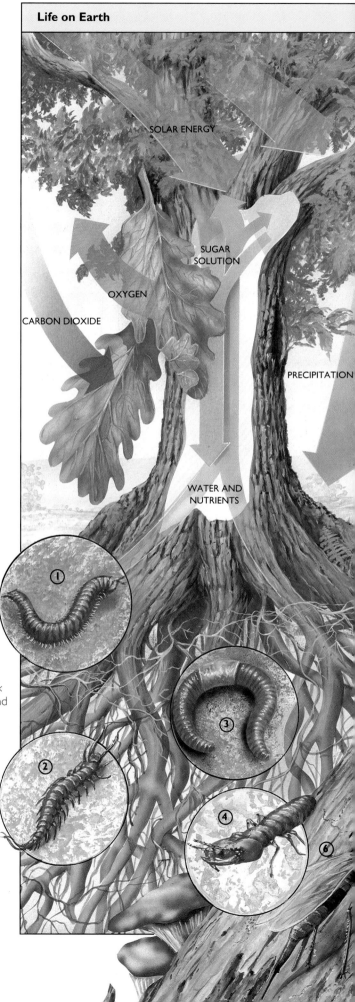

SOLAR ENERGY

SUGAR SOLUTION

OXYGEN

CARBON DIOXIDE

PRECIPITATION

WATER AND NUTRIENTS

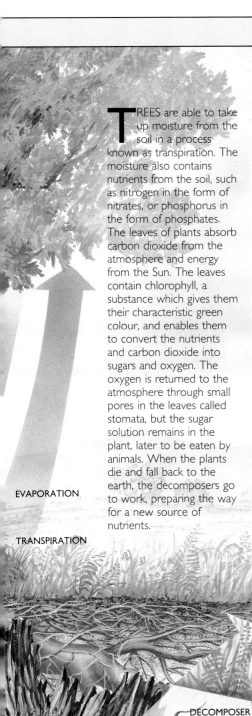

TREES are able to take up moisture from the soil in a process known as transpiration. The moisture also contains nutrients from the soil, such as nitrogen in the form of nitrates, or phosphorus in the form of phosphates. The leaves of plants absorb carbon dioxide from the atmosphere and energy from the Sun. The leaves contain chlorophyll, a substance which gives them their characteristic green colour, and enables them to convert the nutrients and carbon dioxide into sugars and oxygen. The oxygen is returned to the atmosphere through small pores in the leaves called stomata, but the sugar solution remains in the plant, later to be eaten by animals. When the plants die and fall back to the earth, the decomposers go to work, preparing the way for a new source of nutrients.

EVAPORATION

TRANSPIRATION

Nitrogen cycle

Nitrogen is the most abundant gas in the Earth's atmosphere. Other gases, such as oxygen, argon and carbon dioxide are also present. As a single molecule consisting of two nitrogen atoms, nitrogen cannot be taken up by plants. To be useful, it has to be 'fixed'. This fixation involves the action of microorganisms, or bacteria, which live in the soil. They oxidize the nitrogen to form nitrate, which can be used by plants. The nitrates pass into plants and are then eaten by animals. Thus nitrogen atoms are passed around, eventually returning to the atmosphere following the death of animals and plants.

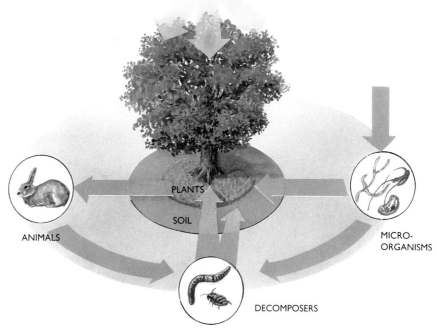

PLANTS

SOIL

ANIMALS

MICRO-ORGANISMS

DECOMPOSERS

Food webs

Living creatures, plants and microorganisms are organized as complex sets of interconnected groups, passing energy in the form of food from one level to the next. Plants produce the food initially, by the process of photosynthesis, and the plants are then consumed by herbivores. Herbivores, such as cows and rabbits, only eat plant matter. Herbivores are then consumed by the secondary consumers, the carnivores or meat-eaters. Many small birds are secondary consumers, as are some rodents such as rats. The secondary consumers are eaten by tertiary consumers or top carnivores.

HERBIVORE

PLANTS

SECONDARY CONSUMER

DECOMPOSER

Decomposers

When plants die they fall to the ground and gradually decay. Living organisms in and on the surface of the soil speed up the process of decomposition. Microscopic organisms include fungi, algae and bacteria. Larger creatures such as earthworms and termites break up plant remains by eating them.

TERTIARY CONSUMER

Large-eyed, hook-beaked owls are top carnivores, feeding on mice, voles and small birds. Owls are generally nocturnal, hunting only at night.

THE LIVING OCEANS

Close to land
The edges of the oceans support many plant species. Sheltered muddy coasts house salt marsh plants in the temperate regions of the world and mangrove plants in the tropics. Below the water level live many sea grasses, providing shelter for a wide range of animals. Large seaweed, known as kelp, is especially useful to the sea otter which sleeps safe from moving currents, using a thick band of kelp as its anchor.

MOST of the world is covered by oceans. The two greatest oceans, the Atlantic and Pacific, cover just over 50 per cent between them. The coastlines, where sea and land meet, are constantly changing shape as sea water eats into the land. Over long periods the position of the world's coastlines also changes as the level of the sea rises and falls. During the last ice age, when large volumes of water were locked up in huge ice sheets, the sea level was 180 metres lower than at present. The Baltic Sea was ice-covered and it was possible to walk between England and France, as well as between Russia and Alaska, using land bridges created by the lowered sea level.

The great ocean basins contain the world's greatest mountains, as well as the deepest trenches. The Mid-Atlantic

Marine ecosystem
The basis of all marine life is found in the phytoplankton which drift around in the sea. These tiny, single-celled organisms, no larger than one millimetre across, contain chlorophyll which enables them to produce vegetable matter from minerals, using energy from the Sun. The sea contains vast numbers of phyto-plankton, consumed by zoo-plankton, small prawns and jellyfish. Larger fish, seals and whales, in turn consume these tiny creatures.

Atoll formation
Several types of coral reef can be found in the world's oceans. Fringing reefs hug the land and often form a ring round recently formed volcanic islands. Barrier reefs are separated from the land by a wide lagoon, often growing up from a deep rocky platform as the sea level rises. If the coral grows as fast as the sea rises, the coral is left in the form of an atoll when the land has disappeared.

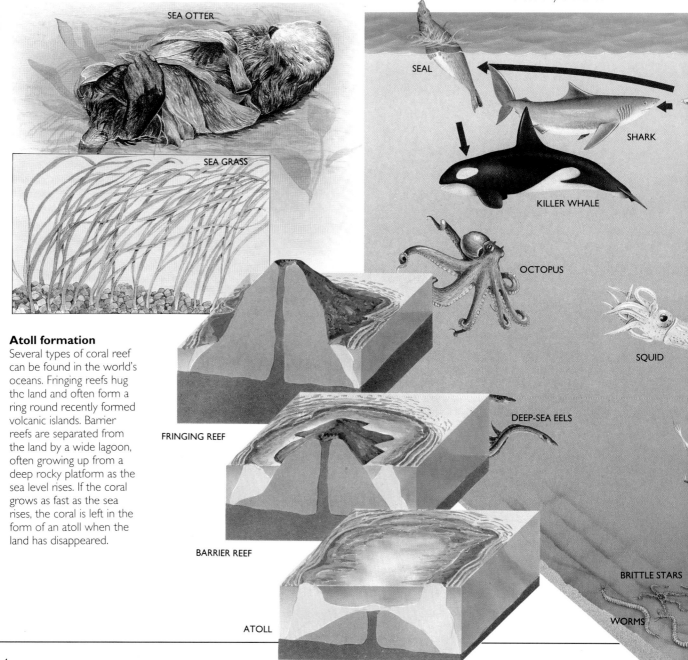

SEA OTTER

SEA GRASS

SEAL

SHARK

KILLER WHALE

OCTOPUS

SQUID

DEEP-SEA EELS

FRINGING REEF

BARRIER REEF

ATOLL

BRITTLE STARS

WORMS

The ocean depths exhibit zones in which certain species survive. Most life can be found in the region down to 200 metres where most sunlight is found. In the middle of the oceanic basins or in trenches, the water is so deep sunlight cannot penetrate. Various creatures, however, survive in the darkness, including sea cucumbers, molluscs and worms.

ridge, forming the junction between two diverging plates and running right along the centre of the Atlantic Ocean, contains mountains higher than the highest on land. They break through the surface to form volcanic islands.

The oceans act as great machines transferring heat from the equator to the poles, in the same way as the atmosphere. As cold and warm ocean currents circulate around the globe the waters meet and mix, greatly affecting the world's weather patterns. The different temperatures also determine the distribution of the rich marine life which inhabits the oceans.

Tides

The gravitational pull of the Moon on the Earth causes the surface of the ocean to bulge on either side of the Earth. The Moon orbits the Earth once every day. As it does so, both bulges move with it, and two tidal cycles are experienced in most parts of the world.

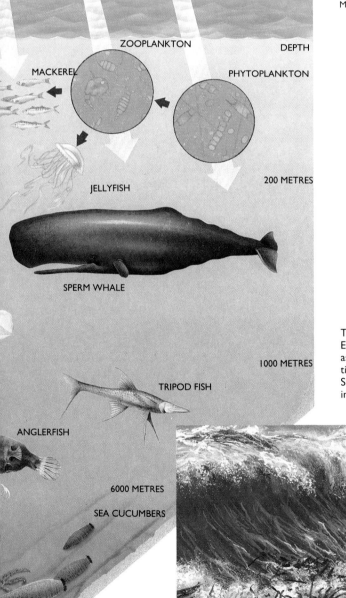

ZOOPLANKTON

MACKEREL

PHYTOPLANKTON

DEPTH

JELLYFISH

200 METRES

SPERM WHALE

1000 METRES

TRIPOD FISH

ANGLERFISH

6000 METRES

SEA CUCUMBERS

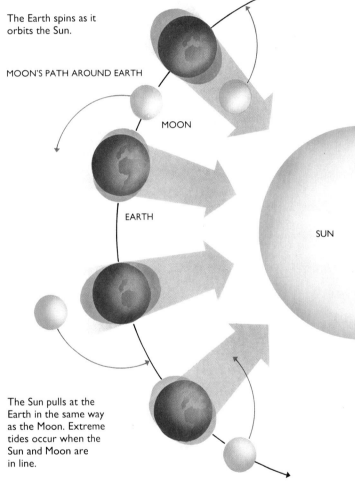

EARTH'S PATH AROUND SUN

The Earth spins as it orbits the Sun.

MOON'S PATH AROUND EARTH

MOON

EARTH

SUN

The Sun pulls at the Earth in the same way as the Moon. Extreme tides occur when the Sun and Moon are in line.

Tsunami

It is unfortunate that tsunamis are also referred to as tidal waves. In fact, tsunamis are generated by earth tremors, known as seismic shocks, and have nothing to do with the gravitational processes that produce tides. They contain a huge amount of energy which is frequently discharged over the land when the wave breaks. They can also travel vast distances across open ocean at speeds of over 900 kilometres per hour. Many are created around the Pacific coast where there is considerable seismic activity beneath the ocean.

NORTH AMERICA

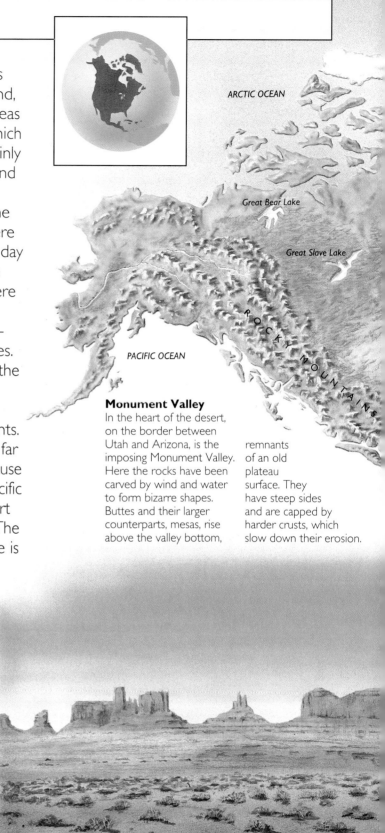

THE continent of North America contains baking deserts, wide expanses of grassland, deciduous and coniferous woodlands, areas of tundra in the far north and some regions which are permanently ice-covered. The climate is mainly responsible for this variation in the landscape and the plants that grow.

In the south-west of North America are the deserts, such as the Mohave and Sonoran, where the temperature reaches over 50°C during the day and many years can pass without rainfall. In the deserts it can be very cold at night because there are no clouds to trap the heat. As with other continents the deserts are surrounded by grasslands, which in North America are called prairies. More rain falls and temperatures are cooler in the prairies and so thousands of grass species can grow. Animals can survive more easily too and the prairies contain many insects and rodents.

Closer to the coasts, the climates become far less harsh, except where cold ocean currents cause the nearby air to remain very dry. Along the Pacific coast, the cold Californian current creates desert conditions which stretch for many kilometres. The North Atlantic is warmer and the coast's climate is more humid so that deciduous woodland can grow. However, as in Europe, much of this woodland has been chopped down to provide land for agriculture.

ARCTIC OCEAN

Great Bear Lake

Great Slave Lake

ROCKY MOUNTAINS

PACIFIC OCEAN

Monument Valley
In the heart of the desert, on the border between Utah and Arizona, is the imposing Monument Valley. Here the rocks have been carved by wind and water to form bizarre shapes. Buttes and their larger counterparts, mesas, rise above the valley bottom, remnants of an old plateau surface. They have steep sides and are capped by harder crusts, which slow down their erosion.

1. The large island of Greenland is covered mainly by ice all year round.
2. The St Lawrence Seaway trading route was formed by glacial erosion of the valley.
3. The five Great Lakes on the USA-Canadian border were formed when ice swept over the land, creating great depressions, which were filled with water.
4. The oldest trees in the world are found on the White Mountains in California: some are up to 4600 years old.
5. Death Valley receives less than 5 centimetres of rain every year. It also has the highest temperatures in the country, reaching up to 57°C.
6. The Gulf of Mexico is the largest gulf in the world.
7. The island of Martinique contains many volcanoes. Its highest is Mount Pelée at 1463 metres, which erupted in 1902 killing 40,000 people.

Coal deposits were formed in ancient Carboniferous swamps. The Okefenokee Swamp in the United States is a similar kind of swamp which exists today. It shows us how swamps may have looked 300 million years ago. Much of the Okefenokee is protected as a refuge for wildlife. Along with many animals and other birds, the great egret stalks the shallow water looking for fish.

HUDSON BAY

ATLANTIC OCEAN

Saskatchewan

L. Winnipeg

St. Lawrence

L. Superior

L. Ontario

L. Huron

Niagara Falls

L. Michigan

L. Erie

APPALACHIAN MOUNTAINS

PRAIRIES

Missouri

Mississippi

Okefenokee Swamp

SIERRA NEVADA

GREAT BASIN

GREATER ANTILLES

MONUMENT VALLEY

LESSER ANTILLES

GRAND CANYON

MOHAVE DESERT

Colorado

Rio Grande

SONORAN DESERT

MEXICAN PLATEAU

GULF OF MEXICO

CARIBBEAN SEA

EL CHICHON

GULF OF CALIFORNIA

Animals in the cold

Many animals have adapted to the harsh arctic environment. There are about 20,000 polar bears living in the Arctic alone. They construct cosy snow dens in which to rear their young and travel across the water using detached ice as rafts, floating thousands of kilometres out to sea.

Unlike much of North America at present, Greenland is covered in ice. It is thought to be the largest island in the world, but if it were possible to strip away the huge ice-sheet which covers the region, we might well discover that underneath there is a series of small islands, rather than one large land mass. Greenland boasts the fastest measured glacier, the Quarayaq Glacier, which moves between 20 and 24 metres every day.

During the Pleistocene period, which lasted from 2 million to 10,000 years ago, huge ice sheets swept down from the Arctic,

The Eternal Fjord

THE magnificent, ice-filled Eternal Fjord in Greenland is 80 kilometres long and has been eroded by flowing ice for over 2 million years. The ice comes from two vast ice-caps in western Greenland, which collect new snow every year. The snow turns to ice and its weight pushes the glaciers outwards from the ice-caps. As they travel, the glaciers cut away at the valleys, making them deeper. Frost-shattered rock falls from the valley walls above the ice, and is carried along in the flow. The valley glaciers eventually reach the sea where they melt and huge blocks of ice break free to float away. Where the glaciers reach the sea they form deep, narrow inlets, or fjords, such as along Greenland's coastline.

Northern lights

Summertime in the far north of the world is marked by a spectacular solar phenomenon. The aurora borealis, or northern lights, are a brilliant display of multicoloured lights in the sky. They can stretch upwards for 100 kilometres into the sky, and can be observed from places thousands of kilometres apart. The aurora is seen when particles from space smash into the Earth's atmosphere, giving out light. The aurora can also be seen in the southern hemisphere, where it is called the aurora australis, or southern lights.

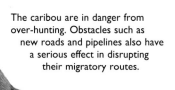

The caribou are in danger from over-hunting. Obstacles such as new roads and pipelines also have a serious effect in disrupting their migratory routes.

Canada's icy past

MOVING from north to south in Canada today, you would find a varied landscape, changing from snow and ice, to tundra, forest and grassland. However, ice sheets covered the whole region in the past and left their mark on the landscape. They carried boulders south and dropped them as the ice melted. Tunnels in the ice left long winding ridges of earth and rock, called eskers, that stretch for several kilometres across the land.

The blue line on the map shows how far ice extended across North America in the last ice age.

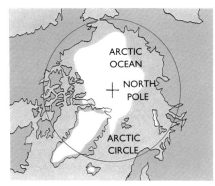

ARCTIC OCEAN

NORTH POLE

ARCTIC CIRCLE

ERRATIC

ESKER

GLACIAL LAKES

ICE AND SNOW

TUNDRA

FOREST AND GRASSLAND

Arctic flowers
In the bleak, desolate Arctic hardy flowers appear and flourish. They are adapted to withstand intense cold and relatively dry conditions. Fine hairs protect flowers from the cold and tight clusters of flowers form a streamlined shape against the wind.

A great weight of ice can make land sink in places. These depressions can then fill up with water when the ice melts. Landscapes which have been glaciated are frequently dotted with water-filled depressions, known as glacial lakes.

Pingos

LARGE areas of Canada, Alaska and Greenland have features characteristic of tundra landscapes. The tundra is an area where the ground is permanently frozen. Pingos form when water in the ground freezes and expands, forcing the ground-surface and soil to rise. Eventually they collapse, leaving a depression which can fill with water in summer.

Caribou
Many animals migrate to find food at different times of the year. The caribou of northern Canada rely on two habitats. In winter they can be found browsing in the coniferous forests of the south where the climate is warmer, but in the summer as the weather improves and the days grow longer they migrate hundreds of kilometres northwards to tundra regions.

SPRING
AUTUMN

covering Canada, Greenland and large areas of the northern United States of America. This happened at least 17 times as the sheets repeatedly advanced and retreated. As the ice advanced over the land, the crust sank deeper into the mantle because of the extra weight on top. Retreat of the ice has allowed it to rise again, resulting in slight earth tremors which are still felt in the east of the continent.

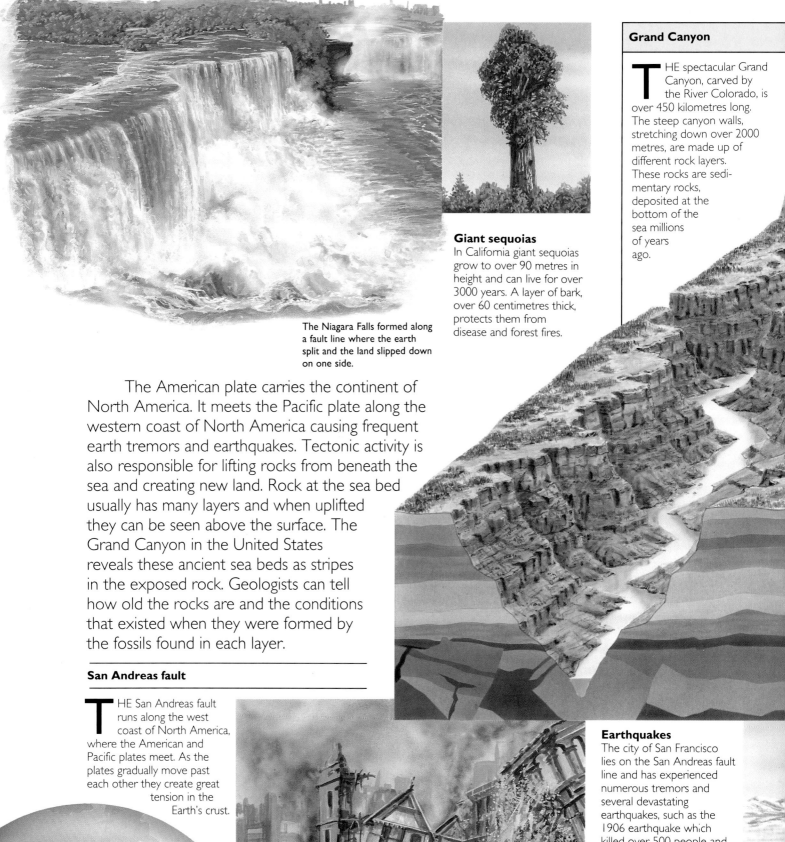

The Niagara Falls formed along a fault line where the earth split and the land slipped down on one side.

Giant sequoias

In California giant sequoias grow to over 90 metres in height and can live for over 3000 years. A layer of bark, over 60 centimetres thick, protects them from disease and forest fires.

Grand Canyon

THE spectacular Grand Canyon, carved by the River Colorado, is over 450 kilometres long. The steep canyon walls, stretching down over 2000 metres, are made up of different rock layers. These rocks are sedimentary rocks, deposited at the bottom of the sea millions of years ago.

The American plate carries the continent of North America. It meets the Pacific plate along the western coast of North America causing frequent earth tremors and earthquakes. Tectonic activity is also responsible for lifting rocks from beneath the sea and creating new land. Rock at the sea bed usually has many layers and when uplifted they can be seen above the surface. The Grand Canyon in the United States reveals these ancient sea beds as stripes in the exposed rock. Geologists can tell how old the rocks are and the conditions that existed when they were formed by the fossils found in each layer.

San Andreas fault

THE San Andreas fault runs along the west coast of North America, where the American and Pacific plates meet. As the plates gradually move past each other they create great tension in the Earth's crust.

NORTH AMERICAN PLATE

PACIFIC PLATE

Earthquakes

The city of San Francisco lies on the San Andreas fault line and has experienced numerous tremors and several devastating earthquakes, such as the 1906 earthquake which killed over 500 people and destroyed large areas of the city. Earthquake severity is measured on a scale known as the Richter scale, which ranges from 1 for a very minor quake, to 8 for massive earth-shaking quakes.

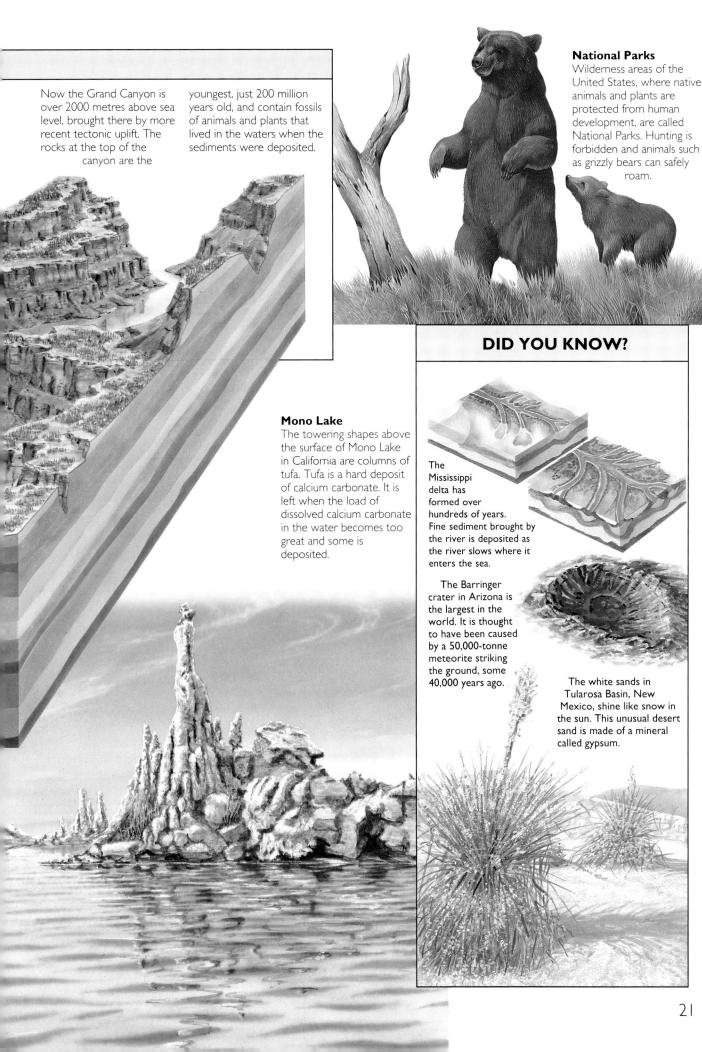

Now the Grand Canyon is over 2000 metres above sea level, brought there by more recent tectonic uplift. The rocks at the top of the canyon are the youngest, just 200 million years old, and contain fossils of animals and plants that lived in the waters when the sediments were deposited.

National Parks
Wilderness areas of the United States, where native animals and plants are protected from human development, are called National Parks. Hunting is forbidden and animals such as grizzly bears can safely roam.

Mono Lake
The towering shapes above the surface of Mono Lake in California are columns of tufa. Tufa is a hard deposit of calcium carbonate. It is left when the load of dissolved calcium carbonate in the water becomes too great and some is deposited.

DID YOU KNOW?

The Mississippi delta has formed over hundreds of years. Fine sediment brought by the river is deposited as the river slows where it enters the sea.

The Barringer crater in Arizona is the largest in the world. It is thought to have been caused by a 50,000-tonne meteorite striking the ground, some 40,000 years ago.

The white sands in Tularosa Basin, New Mexico, shine like snow in the sun. This unusual desert sand is made of a mineral called gypsum.

Deadly storms

Devastating hurricanes, also known as cyclones or typhoons, occur regularly along the eastern shores of America, Asia and Australia. These huge heat machines, up to 800 kilometres in diameter and with winds of over 100 kilometres per hour, are the world's greatest storms. In the 20th century over 45,000 people have been killed in the Caribbean and south-eastern United States from the activity of hurricanes.

The storms which wreck the shores of eastern central America originate in warm tropical seas, some travelling across the Atlantic Ocean from the western

El Chichón

ON 4th April, 1982, the ancient mountain of El Chichón in Mexico erupted after lying dormant for over one thousand years. The jungle covered dome was blown off in the eruption and a vertical plume of dust, ash and gases was pumped high into the stratosphere.

GULF OF MEXICO

CARIBBEAN SEA

shores of Africa. The warm seas supply heat and water to the air above which rises, sending towering clouds into the sky. Winds, moving in the upper atmosphere, steer the brewing storm towards the islands of the Caribbean, and the rotation of the Earth produces a spinning effect in the rising air. On reaching land, the hurricane's energy supply is

cut off and, in an enormous blast, the energy is released, causing widespread destruction. The heat released in a single storm would supply the United States with power for three years if it could be converted into electricity.

Monarch butterflies

North American monarch butterflies migrate long distances. Born in the Great Lakes area of the United States, they migrate annually, travelling the 4000 kilometres south to California, Florida and Mexico, and then back again in spring.

22

The towering cloud of dust reached a height of over 20 kilometres. It was carried by the strong winds of the upper atmosphere for thousands of kilometres around the globe, reducing solar radiation over a wide area. Near the volcano ash fell like dusty rain and settled, covering the land with a thick layer of fine powder. As the volcano erupted, dangerously high levels of poisonous gases were also released.

SHOWER OF ASH

Waterspout

Intense low pressure cells, or tornadoes, over the sea create waterspouts. As the tornado passes across the sea surface, huge quantities of water can be sucked up into a rising, swirling mass that towers into the sky. When this water returns to the Earth it creates a salty rainstorm which can deluge large areas with seawater. Any fish sucked up with the water will also be dropped. Several waterspouts have been seen off the coast of Florida in the Atlantic Ocean and in the Gulf of Mexico.

Crown-of-thorns

The crown-of-thorns starfish feeds off living coral polyps and so is a major threat to coral reefs. At present they inhabit the Indian and Pacific Oceans but with the opening of the Panama Canal a passageway to the Caribbean has been provided. It is feared that this may eventually lead to an attack on the coral reefs in the region.

The continents of North and South America are joined by the narrow isthmus or 'land bridge' of Central America. The connection was made from 5 to 2 million years ago. Before this, parts of Central America and the Greater Antilles islands of the Caribbean were joined to form a smaller single landmass. The land was broken up by erosion and movements in the Earth's crust. The movement and collision of plates continues to effect the region as can be seen from the numerous earthquakes and volcanic eruptions on the isthmus of Central America and the islands of the Caribbean.

Bats in the desert

SAGUARO CACTUS

IN the baking hot Sonoran Desert, extending northwards from Mexico, there are many species of cactus. The organ-pipe and saguaro cacti rely on bats for pollination. The lesser long-nosed bats drink the sweet nectar of their flowers, pollinating them as they cross the desert. Later the bats return to feed on the succulent cactus fruits, the results of their last journey through the desert.

ORGAN-PIPE CACTUS

Grey whale migration

Every year the grey whale undertakes the longest migration of any mammal, travelling 20,400 kilometres from the lagoons of Baja California to the Bering Sea and back again. It averages a speed of just 8 kilometres per hour. The calves are born in the winter at the southernmost point of the route near Mexico. In spring the whales set off northwards and reach their summer feeding ground several months later.

FEEDING GROUNDS
→ MIGRATION ROUTES

SAGUARO FLOWER

SOUTH AMERICA

L. Maracaibo

Panama
Canal

THE South American continent is sandwiched between the world's two mighty oceans, the Atlantic to the east and the Pacific to the west. The continent's southern tip tapers to a very narrow point, just 800 kilometres across. It is called Cape Horn and ancient round-the-world sea voyages had to negotiate the Cape's stormy waters to get from ocean to ocean. Today, the Panama Canal, just 64 kilometres long, allows ships to cross the continent, without having to go on the lengthy voyage around South America.

Along the west coast of South America is the long, high Andean mountain chain. The Andes mountains are very active, with frequent phases of uplift and much volcanic activity. Lake Titicaca, the world's highest large lake, is tucked between the peaks of Peru and Bolivia, high in the mountains.

South America also contains the world's largest rainforest. Seventy-five per cent of South America is tropical and most of it is also humid which provides the ideal environment for the growth of dense, tall and extensive rainforests. Most of the rainforest is in Brazil and is called the Amazon rainforest.

Andes and condors
Soaring high into the skies above the South American Andes a strange species of vulture, known as the condor, is sometimes seen. These birds of prey roost in crevices and on ledges on the steep mountain sides, swooping into the sky on rising updrafts of air. The condors are impressive in flight, with broad wings, short necks and heavy wedge-like tails. The surface area of their wings is over 2 square metres. They avoid areas of human habitation and are only seen in a narrow strip of land between Ecuador and Cape Horn.

1. Colombia is the wettest country on Earth, receiving around 12,000 millimetres of rain every year.

2. The Amazon in flood discharges 200,000 cubic metres of water into the Atlantic Ocean every second. It has the greatest flow of any river in the world.

3. Lake Titicaca is the largest lake in South America. It is 3800 metres above sea level, making it the highest big lake in the world.

4. The Atacama Desert in Chile has suffered the longest drought ever recorded, with 400 years between rainstorms.

5. Mount Aconcagua in Argentina is the highest mountain in South America at 6960 metres.

Orinoco

Angel Falls

Negro

Amazon

AMAZON RAINFOREST

Amazon

Purus

Xingu

Tocantins

Araguaia

Sao Francisco

BRAZILIAN HIGHLANDS

ANDES

Parana

PACIFIC OCEAN

GRAN CHACO

ATACAMA DESERT

SIERRA DE CORDOBA

PAMPAS

ATLANTIC OCEAN

FALKLAND ISLANDS

CAPE HORN

River Amazon

The world's second longest river, the Amazon, snakes its way through the dense tropical forests. Its path shows that the river alters its course frequently, curving this way and that, leaving old, cut-off channels to be gradually colonized by plants.

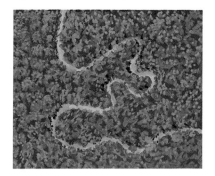

In the Pacific Ocean, 1300 kilometres west of South America, are the Galapagos Islands, formed by volcanic activity. British scientist, Charles Darwin, visited these islands in 1830 and it was this expedition that inspired his famous theory of evolution. Darwin was able to study astounding animal adaptations that enabled some species to exploit and survive in their habitat more effectively than others. Each of the 15 Galapagos islands is unique, some are dry and bare, others are moist and luxuriant. Through time, animals on each have altered as they change their behaviour to make the most of such diverse environments.

Andes rainshadow

FLOWING from south to north off the west coast of South America is the cold Humboldt (or Peruvian) ocean current, transferring water away from the Antarctic. Above the cold sea, the air is cooled, clouds form, and the air sheds a lot of its moisture. As the air blows inland, warmer conditions over the land heat the air and it becomes very dry. Forced to rise over the Andes, the cooling air expels the remaining water vapour which condenses, forms clouds and falls to the ground as rain. Descending air on the

2. Any water vapour left in the cool air condenses to form clouds.

ANDES

1. Warm, dry air cools as it is forced up over the Andes.

FRIGATE BIRD

Galapagos Island wildlife

The range of environments in the Galapagos Islands has given rise to an amazing diversity in the colonizing species. Even animals of the same type vary in colour and size from island to island. Among the unusual creatures of Galapagos are the giant tortoises, sea lions, land and marine iguanas and Galapagos penguins. There is a huge variety of birds, including the frigate bird, the male of which has a red throat pouch which he can inflate in courtship displays.

PACIFIC OCEAN

LAND IGUANA

eastern side of the mountain chain is so dry, permanent desert conditions result. The Patagonia Desert is known as a rainshadow desert because it exists on the lee side of the Andes, in the 'rainshadow' area.

3. Descending air warms up and becomes dry.

4. Dry air passes over the rainshadow desert.

The range of scenery in South America is striking. Either side of the Andean mountain chain lie areas of desert, which contrast markedly with the humid, hot tropical forest of Brazil. In addition to these extremes of aridity and humidity there is the South American pampas, a region of grassland where the climate is too dry to support forest. Here grasses and low-lying flowers flourish in conditions which are similar to the North American prairies.

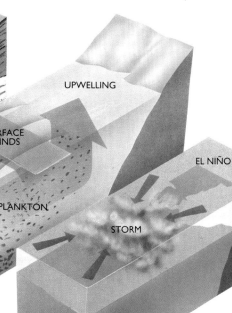

PATAGONIA DESERT

RAINSHADOW

UPWELLING

SURFACE WINDS

PLANKTON

STORM

EL NIÑO

Upwelling

The marine ecosystem of the eastern Pacific depends upon the upwelling of cool water, which brings plankton to the surface to be eaten by fish. Upwelling occurs because winds blow west-ward, taking warm surface water away, allowing it to be replaced by cool water from below.

El Niño and the loss of upwelling means plankton does not rise to the surface, fish die and the fishing industry suffers great losses.

El Niño

Every few years winds weaken over the Pacific and a warm patch of sea called El Niño develops off the Peruvian coast. This creates storms which suck air in from all around. The air keeps the sea warm and upwelling does not occur.

Forests in flames

To gain adequate food from the rainforest a specialized farming technique known as shifting cultivation (or slash-and-burn agriculture) has long been used. First, patches of forest are cleared for cultivation and then burning enriches the soil with nutrients. Once these are used up it is necessary to move to a new area. Tropical rainforests can sustain some clearance but cannot recover quickly from the large-scale destruction which occurs as population numbers increase.

DID YOU KNOW?

South American monkeys, like the red-faced uakari, have wide, flat noses with nostrils facing outwards, either side. In the rest of the world monkeys' noses are thin with their nostrils pointing up or down.

Angel Falls on the Caroní River in Venezuela is the highest waterfall in the world. The water drops from a height of 979 metres down into a gorge.

Disappearing forests

Largescale tree-cutting or logging is increasing at a rapid rate because of the demand for rainforest wood from industrialized nations. The consequences of logging are becoming clear. People whose livelihood depends on food from the forest are being forced from their homes. The trees offer protection to the soil, and so their removal results in soil erosion and flooding. Logging activity also kills wildlife, and leads to the extinction of many species.

TROPICAL FOREST DAMAGED OR DESTROYED SINCE 1940S

TROPICAL FOREST 1980S

I N THE permanently wet tropics dense rainforest vegetation can grow all year round. The main areas of tropical rainforest are in Africa, South America and Southeast Asia. Situated on the equator, it is the most diverse of any land biome, containing over half of the world's known plant species. A biome is a major plant and animal community which extends over a large area. It is alive with creatures, each with a distinctive call, making it an exciting, vibrant and noisy place, especially at night. The rainforest is constantly changing. Its tall trees, supported by their huge buttress roots, are often felled by lightning strikes and forest fires, opening up gaps in the canopy. These gaps are gradually filled by new seedlings, growing into 80 metre-high trees in a hundred years. In the meantime new gaps open up. Seen from the air the rainforest is a patchwork with each area at a different stage of regrowth.

During the Pleistocene glaciations, when conditions were cooler and drier in the tropics,

Inside the forest

Rainforests house a mass of wildlife. Many animals live on the forest floor which is covered by a layer of semi-decomposed and fresh leaves. Bacteria and micro-organisms secrete acids which decompose this litter and allow it to become mixed with the surface soil. The minerals supplied in this way support new plant life.

Layers of the forest

The roof of the forest is a dense canopy of trees which receives large amounts of sunlight and moisture. Here one finds many of the rainforest primates. The tall hardwood trees, called emergents, stretch out

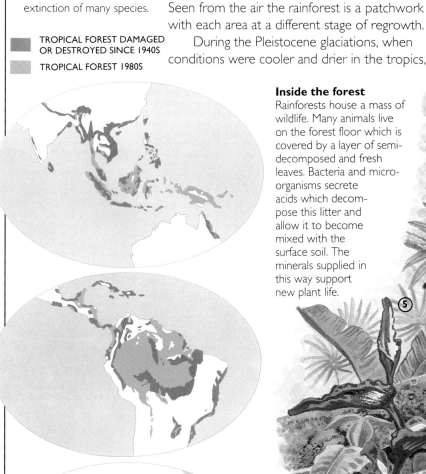

above the canopy top. Below, the forest becomes darker as less sunlight can penetrate the canopy, and trees here do not grow to be as tall. There are also epiphytes, such as lianas, which use the rooting trees for support.

the rainforests retreated to small areas where the plants could survive. After most of the ice had melted and the equatorial regions become warmer, the rainforest spread to its present extent. Today the threat to rainforest survival is coming from human demand for wood and wood products, encouraging people to cut down trees. The rainforest is a delicate ecosystem, with complex food webs. The loss of one type of animal affects many other forest animals.

Animals and birds
1. Swift
2. Toucan
3. Spider monkey
4. Marmoset
5. Scarlet macaw
6. Tree boa
7. Three-toed sloth
8. Morpho butterfly
9. Arrow poison frog
10. Giant armadillo
11. Hercules beetle

Flying squirrels
Every evening at dusk the flying squirrels embark on their perilous journey from tree to tree, gliding through the air supported by thin flaps of skin. They scurry up the tall trees, rush to the end of a protruding branch and launch themselves into the air. In this way they progress through the forest in search of food.

Camouflaged
To survive in the rainforest some insects and animals have developed camouflage techniques. Either they attempt to be invisible to the creatures that prey upon them or they lie in wait for their own tasty meal. With the appearance of a pink flower, the praying mantis blends perfectly with the local plants, sitting motionless, awaiting a passing insect. From afar, thorn bugs look exactly like thorns, coating plants and remaining safely disguised from likely predators.

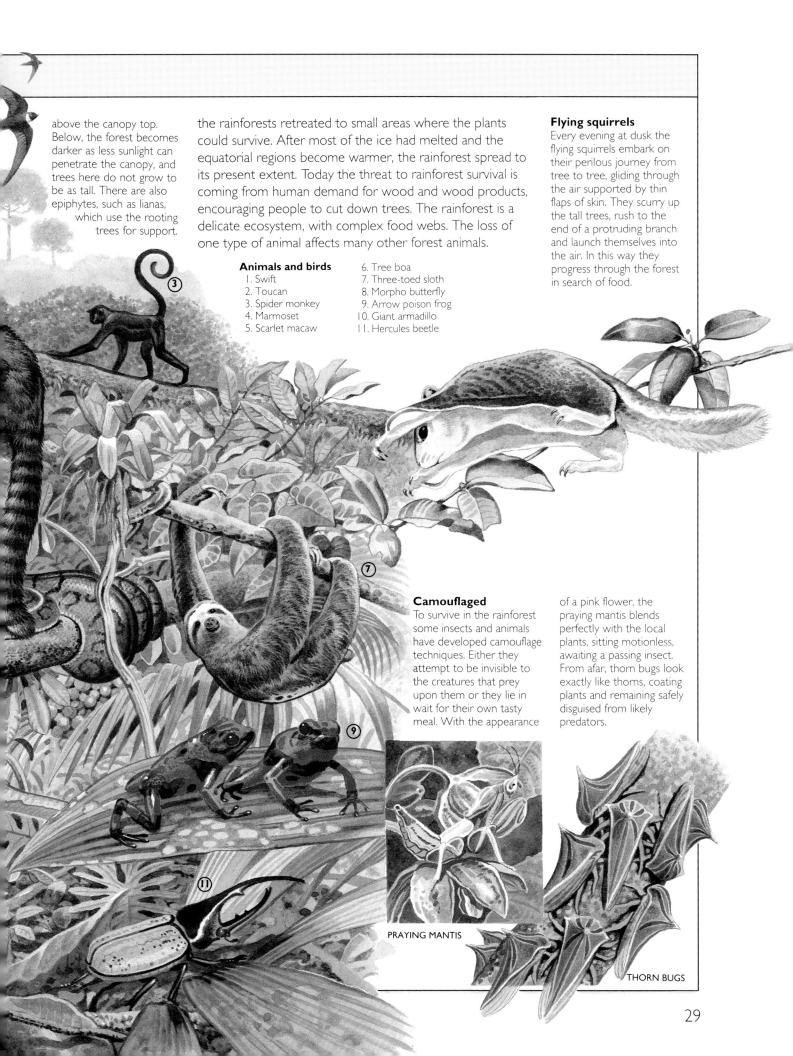

PRAYING MANTIS

THORN BUGS

EUROPE

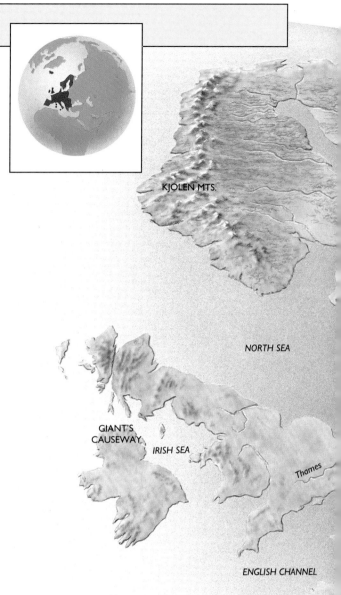

THE continent of Europe is small, second only to Oceania, but its varied rocks and climate give rise to diverse scenery. In the north of Europe ancient mountains are made of resistant volcanic rocks. The younger mountains in the south, the Alps, are composed of folded sedimentary rocks. Large areas of limestone, a sedimentary rock, hide spectacular subterranean caves in many parts of Europe, while in other parts the limestone has been dissolved and etched by water to form deep, steep-sided gorges.

The climate of Europe becomes more seasonal towards the north. In the Mediterranean region, it is hot and dry in summer, but cooler and wetter in winter. In northern Europe, especially inland, the winters can be extremely cold and the summers fairly hot. Also, the day-length changes throughout the year. North of the Arctic Circle there are 24 hours of daylight on midsummer's day, but midwinter's day is completely dark for 24 hours. Such changes in the amount of daylight and the climate influence the types of plants and animals that can live in each region. For example, on moving southwards from the edge of the Arctic ice, the natural vegetation changes firstly to tundra plants, then to coniferous forest, then deciduous forest, and finally to Mediterranean forest in the extreme south.

1. Iceland is called the 'land of frost and fire' – glaciers can be found next to volcanoes.
2. Finland is the most densely forested land in Europe, with two thirds covered in trees.
3. Forty per cent of the Netherlands has been reclaimed from the sea, and is known as the polder lands. The highest point in the Netherlands is just 300 metres above sea level
4. It is possible to travel by river right across Europe from the Black Sea to the North Sea because the Danube is connected to the Rhine by a short canal.
5. The Pyrenees mountain chain forms a natural land barrier between the Iberian Peninsula and the rest of Europe.
6. Marble has been quarried for hundreds of years in Carrara. This beautiful metamorphic stone is carved into statues and decorative building work.
7. The Bosphorus Straits which split the city of Istanbul also separate the continents of Europe and Asia.
8. A famous colony of monkeys lives on the Rock of Gibraltar, a limestone promontory at the tip of southern Spain. The monkeys may have been brought to the Rock by the Romans from North Africa.

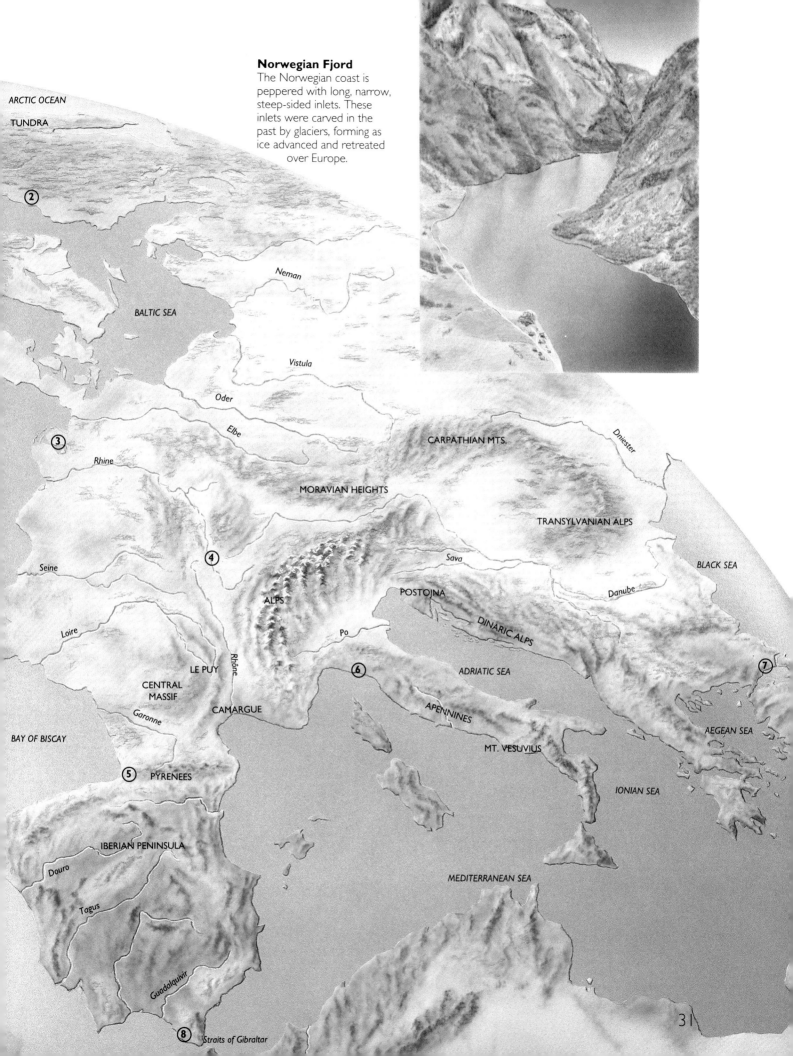

Norwegian Fjord
The Norwegian coast is peppered with long, narrow, steep-sided inlets. These inlets were carved in the past by glaciers, forming as ice advanced and retreated over Europe.

ARCTIC OCEAN

TUNDRA

②

BALTIC SEA

Neman

Vistula

Oder

Elbe

③

Rhine

CARPATHIAN MTS.

Dniester

MORAVIAN HEIGHTS

TRANSYLVANIAN ALPS

④

Seine

Sava

BLACK SEA

ALPS

POSTOJNA

DINARIC ALPS

Danube

Loire

Po

ADRIATIC SEA

⑦

LE PUY

Rhône

⑥

CENTRAL MASSIF

CAMARGUE

APENNINES

AEGEAN SEA

Garonne

BAY OF BISCAY

MT. VESUVIUS

⑤ PYRENEES

IONIAN SEA

IBERIAN PENINSULA

Douro

MEDITERRANEAN SEA

Tagus

Guadalquivir

⑧ Straits of Gibraltar

31

Alpine glaciers

On many Alpine mountains ice forms glaciers as snow melts and refreezes. Every year, as a new layer of snow is added, the extra weight drags the ice down through the valleys. Packed into a valley, a glacier scrapes away at the valley sides, crushing the rock into a fine powder. As the glaciers flow around

protruding rocks, large ice caves form underneath the ice. In places it is possible to sit in the caves and watch the ice flowing past.

Avalanche

Alpine snow can be extremely dangerous, crashing down the mountain slopes, destroying houses. Avalanches are started when snow rapidly accumulates or during spring melting, setting off a chain reaction. An immense weight of snow can plunge down the mountainside at over 250 kilometres per hour, surrounded by a cloud of powdery snow carried in the air.

The Camargue

IN southern France where the River Rhone reaches the Mediterranean Sea there is a vast marshy area of lakes containing both fresh and salty water, called the Camargue. With the loss of large areas of coastal wetlands to agriculture, the Camargue has become increasingly important as a site for breeding and wintering birds. The lagoons are occupied by huge colonies of birds, including flamingoes, purple herons (below left) and terns. Hundreds of tiny tree frogs also live in the nearby reed beds.

Among the many animals found roaming around the delta are herds of wild horses. These graceful animals, born with black, red or brown colouring, turn white as they approach adulthood.

PURPLE HERON

The European continent is separated from Africa by the Mediterranean Sea. The European and African plates collided and formed the Alps in south-west Europe. The continued movement of these plates also causes earthquakes in Italy, Yugoslavia and Greece, and has built the Atlas mountains in north-west Africa. The island of Crete in the Mediterranean, which lies where the plates meet, has been slowly tilting because of the continuing crust movement. The western edge of the island has raised shorelines, while in the east harbours built by the ancient Romans have sunk into the sea.

The coastlines of Europe vary widely. In northern Spain there are steep, rocky cliffs and in southern France we find the flat marshes of the Camargue. Britain has many cliffs of soft rocks, which often slide into the sea.

The Giant's Causeway

More than 40,000 hexagonal columns over 15 metres tall make up the Giant's Causeway in Northern Ireland. Volcanic activity caused the formation of the Giant's Causeway when molten rock forced its way to the Earth's surface and poured out over the land as lava. When the lava cooled at the surface, it contracted and cracked to form the hexagons we see today.

The thin, free-flowing lava that created the Giant's Causeway is called basaltic lava. Thicker lava, called andesitic lava, forms steep-sided volcanic cones as it cannot flow so far and solidifies into granite, a hard, resistant rock.

Le Puy

Molten rock which has escaped to the surface of the Earth and solidified is very resistant to erosion. Molten rock can be injected into an opening or vent, forming a 'plug'. The plug may be left standing when surrounding rock has been eroded away. *Puy* is French for 'plug' and such features are particularly common in south-central France.

DID YOU KNOW?

The hardened ash around Mount Vesuvius in Italy contains perfectly preserved human shapes, buried by ash from an eruption of the mountain almost 2000 years ago, in AD79.

The islands of Santorini are the remains of an ancient volcanic mountain. Its top was blown off in a gigantic explosion around 3500 years ago. The islands are part of the rim of the remaining crater.

Danger at sea

THE billions of tonnes of sewage added to the Mediterranean is a danger to marine life. The sewage cannot escape through the Straits of Gibraltar and so accumulates as tourism expands. The Valencia tooth carp that lives along the coast of eastern Spain is almost extinct. Animals like the fur seal are threatened by other waste products.

VALENCIA TOOTH CARP

FUR SEAL

Disappearing villages

Coastal erosion is a problem in many parts of Europe. Whole villages – even if built far from the coastline – can disappear as the sea cuts away at the land, in places at up to a metre every year. Several factors combine to cause such rapid land loss. For example, cliffs made of very soft rock in a highly exposed location erode dangerously fast.

33

Trapped in amber

Insects, thousands of years old, can sometimes be found preserved in amber, a fossil resin from ancient trees. This spider lived in the Baltic pine forests during the Pleistocene period.

During the last ice age the great weight of ice made the land in northern Europe sink slightly into the Earth's molten mantle. When the ice melted at the end of the ice age the land was released from its heavy burden and gradually began to rise. All the ice had left Europe 10,000 years ago, but the land has taken so long to rise, parts of northern Scandinavia are still lifting, in places by over 5 millimetres every year.

Mid-Atlantic ridge

The volcanic Mid-Atlantic ridge runs through the centre of Iceland in the northern Atlantic Ocean. Here the plates are separating, opening up fissures in the crust allowing volcanic lava to escape to the surface. Iceland is covered with erupting volcanoes and the nearby volcanic island of Surtsey rose from the sea in 1963. Water heated by magma under Iceland's surface rises as a steaming bubble at Strokkur, and bursts, to become Iceland's greatest geyser.

Limestone scenery

ON THE surface limestone scenery is often marked by pavements of bare rock and little water, as streams disappear below the surface to flow underground. It is beneath the surface that limestone scenery is most impressive, with caves, channels and ornate deposits of calcite. There are 7000 known caves in Yugoslavia, Croatia and Serbia and the largest, at Postojna, is called the Concert Hall. It contains spectacular hanging stalactites and towering stalagmites.

Rainwater is slightly acidic and can dissolve the calcium carbonate in limestone. As

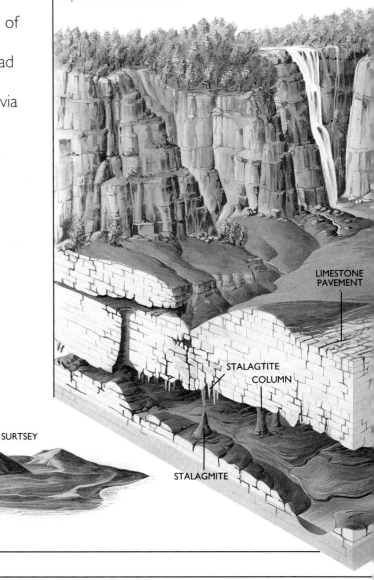

LIMESTONE PAVEMENT

STALAGTITE COLUMN

STALAGMITE

SURTSEY

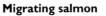

Migrating salmon

EVERY year the North Atlantic salmon makes two or three long migrations from ocean to river in order to spawn. The spawning territory of the salmon has been reduced by recreational salmon fishing, overfishing in coastal areas and pollution of rivers in industrialized countries. As a result salmon has completely disappeared from the rivers of Germany, southern England and New England. In an attempt to conserve the salmon, large-scale fishing, such as drift-netting, has been made illegal.

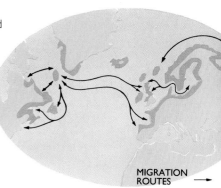

MIGRATION ROUTES

the acid runs into the rock through cracks, joints and bedding planes, it works away at the walls, enlarging the joints and opening up channels. Large areas of rock are dissolved away to form caves deep under the ground. If the water picks up more calcium carbonate than it can carry, some will precipitate out to form stalactites and stalagmites as it drops from the cave roof and walls. Eventually the roof may collapse to reveal steep-sided gorges and small streams super-charged with calcium carbonate.

Midnight sun
Swedish lapland is also known as the 'land of the midnight sun' because the Sun never sets in mid-summer. The story is very different during the winter months, when the Sun barely rises and darkness falls early in the day. This change in the amount of daylight occurs because the Earth tilts as it orbits the Sun.

The landscape of northern and eastern Europe includes the tundra in the far north and the boreal forests further south. Moving eastwards across the continent further from the sea, the climate becomes drier and grasslands replace forests.

Many countries in Europe are highly industrialized and pollution has been a problem for many years, affecting wildlife and damaging forests. Many forests have also been cut down for timber and to provide land for farming. This has been happening for so long most of the natural deciduous wood-lands of Europe have completely disappeared.

LIMESTONE GORGES

SINKHOLE

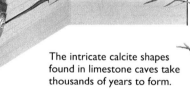

The intricate calcite shapes found in limestone caves take thousands of years to form.

UNDERGROUND STREAM

Acid rain
Emissions of sulphur dioxide from industrial plants can have serious effects on the ecology of many areas. Sulphur dioxide easily combines with rainwater to form a dilute sulphuric acid, which is more acidic than vinegar. Tall chimneys pump gases high into the troposphere where they can then be carried over great distances. The westerly airflows over Europe mean that acidic emissions from one country may cause damage many hundreds of kilometres away in other countries. The greatest effects are felt where the soil is thin and already acidic, often where coniferous forests grow. The trees become stunted and the acidic runoff reaching rivers and lakes can also damage plant and animal life.

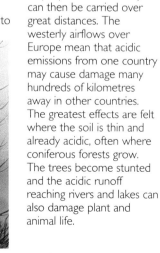

ASIA

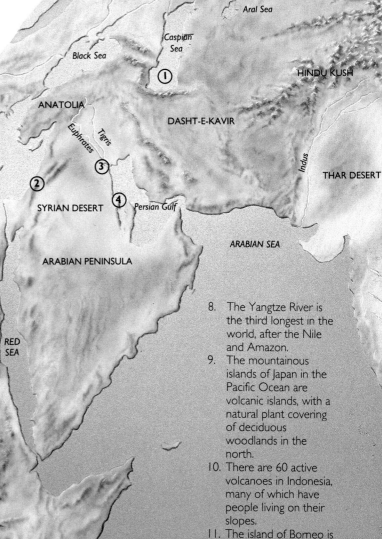

THE huge Asian continent contains a large number of record-breaking physical features. Within its 43 million square kilometres there is the highest mountain, the deepest lake, the largest inland sea, the third longest river and the third largest island in the world. From the top of Mount Everest to the bottom of Lake Baikal the height change is over 10.5 kilometres. From west to east, Asia stretches from the Arabian Peninsula to the Indonesian Archipelago, a distance of over 8000 kilometres. An archipelago is a group of islands, and that of Indonesia consists of over 13,000 islands dotted around the south-west Pacific.

The collision of the Indian and Eurasian plates has buckled and squeezed the rocks in Asia, lifting them over 8 kilometres into the sky to form the Himalayan mountain chain. These mountains are still forming today as the Indian plate continues its northward journey. However, as the upward motion of the rocks continues, so too do the forces of downward movement resulting from the action of water and ice, which rapidly erode the peaks.

5. The country of Nepal is situated in the Himalayas and 90 per cent of its area is covered by mountain slopes.

6. The world's heaviest hailstones ever recorded fell on Bangladesh on 14 April 1986. They killed over 90 people.
7. Lake Baikal is the deepest lake in the world. In places it is almost 2 kilometres deep.

1. The Caspian Sea is the largest inland sea in the world. It covers an area of 371,000 square kilometres.
2. The Dead Sea is seven times saltier than the oceans. Its shoreline is 395 metres below sea level.
3. There are no permanent lakes or rivers in Kuwait – the country is entirely desert.
4. Oil was first discovered in 1932 in Bahrain, the first state in the Persian Gulf to become oil-rich.

8. The Yangtze River is the third longest in the world, after the Nile and Amazon.
9. The mountainous islands of Japan in the Pacific Ocean are volcanic islands, with a natural plant covering of deciduous woodlands in the north.
10. There are 60 active volcanoes in Indonesia, many of which have people living on their slopes.
11. The island of Borneo is the world's third largest island.

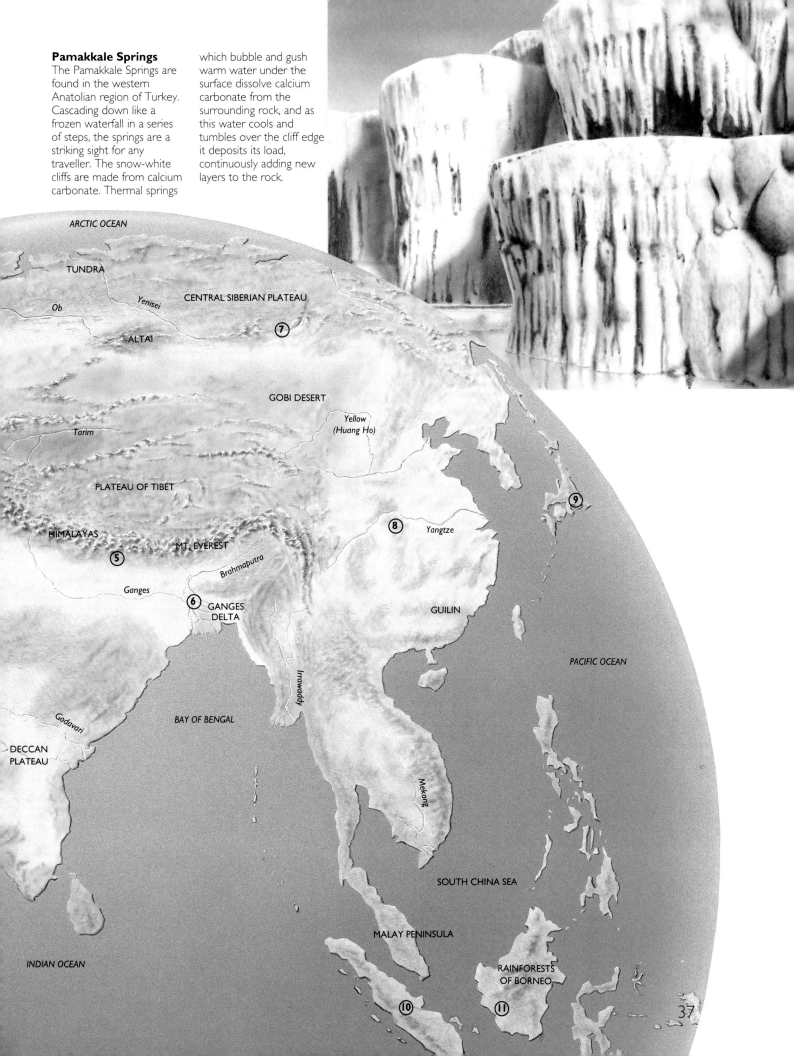

Pamakkale Springs

The Pamakkale Springs are found in the western Anatolian region of Turkey. Cascading down like a frozen waterfall in a series of steps, the springs are a striking sight for any traveller. The snow-white cliffs are made from calcium carbonate. Thermal springs which bubble and gush warm water under the surface dissolve calcium carbonate from the surrounding rock, and as this water cools and tumbles over the cliff edge it deposits its load, continuously adding new layers to the rock.

ARCTIC OCEAN

TUNDRA

Ob

Yenisei

CENTRAL SIBERIAN PLATEAU

⑦

ALTAI

GOBI DESERT

Yellow
(Huang Ho)

Tarim

PLATEAU OF TIBET

⑨

⑧ Yangtze

HIMALAYAS

MT. EVEREST

⑤

Brahmaputra

Ganges

⑥ GANGES
DELTA

GUILIN

Irrawaddy

Godavari

BAY OF BENGAL

PACIFIC OCEAN

DECCAN
PLATEAU

Mekong

SOUTH CHINA SEA

MALAY PENINSULA

INDIAN OCEAN

RAINFORESTS
OF BORNEO

⑩

⑪

Haboobs

In Arabia sand and dust storms are common. They are known as haboobs, from the Arabic word *Haab*, meaning 'to blow'. Wind speeds of 5 metres per second can set large sand grains in motion.

The western extreme of Asia consists of the Middle East and the Arabian Peninsula. Most of the region is desert, although the Tigris and Euphrates rivers run through fertile plains. On the Arabian Peninsula there are no permanent streams and water has to be drawn from wells, dug deep to reach the groundwater supply. Because of the heat evaporation rates are high and there is a constant need for water to irrigate the land. Some of the world's hottest deserts, such as the Dasht-e-Kavir and Rub al-Khali, are found in the region. Oman, on the east of the

Gulf War pollution

THE Persian Gulf is one of the world's most polluted waterways. Survival in the salty, oil-laden waters is difficult but several species manage to inhabit the Gulf. In the shallow seas on its western edge algae, the life support of many fish, thrive. However, sea currents and north-westerly winds drive the polluted water along the Saudi coast where it accumulates. In the 1991 Gulf War, damage to the environment reached incredible levels, with large quantities of oil pouring from pipelines into the

A disappearing sea

The shrinking of the Aral Sea is one of the worst environmental disasters of the 20th century. Since 1960, when water started to be extracted to irrigate the surrounding desert for cotton production, over 40 per cent of its surface area has vanished, a volume of water which would fill Lake Erie in North America one and a half times. Over 28,500 square kilometres of sea-bed is now a barren wasteland of sand and salt. People living nearby suffer from respiratory diseases and throat cancer from the dust. A once thriving fishing trade no longer exists and ships lie marooned on the shores of the lake.

1960

1971

1987

shallow waters. Some spills were over a kilometre long and nearly a metre deep, killing thousands of birds like the cormorant and threatening fragile coral reefs. As oil fields were set alight, the land was scorched and many desert animals perished.

🐦 CORMORANT AND TERN BREEDING AREAS

🐢 TURTLE NEST SITES

OIL SPILL

IMPERMEABLE ROCK

POROUS ROCK

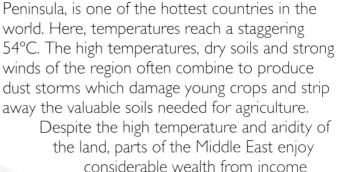

Peninsula, is one of the hottest countries in the world. Here, temperatures reach a staggering 54°C. The high temperatures, dry soils and strong winds of the region often combine to produce dust storms which damage young crops and strip away the valuable soils needed for agriculture.

Despite the high temperature and aridity of the land, parts of the Middle East enjoy considerable wealth from income based on the vast oil reserves in the region.

Oil formation
Oil and natural gas are made up from hydrocarbons. All organisms contain some hydrocarbons and as dead organisms accumulate, usually on the bed of the sea, the hydrocarbons become concentrated and compressed. Hydrocarbons exist as liquids (oil) and gases (natural gas). As they are compressed, both migrate through the pores of permeable rocks, such as sandstone and limestone. But if they reach an impermeable barrier, such as a layer of shale, they cannot continue to move. Trapped, they become a valuable source of fuel as in many parts of the Middle East.

Dead Sea salts
Around the edge of the Dead Sea are accumulations of salt crystals, coating the rocks like icing on a cake. Constantly supplied with salts from the Earth's interior, the sea's water has been unable to contain them, so a large number solidify.

DID YOU KNOW?

Sand dunes in the desert can be shaped as stars. It is not known exactly why this happens, but it is thought to be due to winds extending the dunes in different directions.

Locusts are edible grass-hoppers found in Africa and Asia. They migrate in huge swarms, completely devouring the vegetation of the regions they cross.

ANIMALS IN DANGER

African elephants
In 1900 African elephants roamed across vast areas of the African continent and were found within a continuous belt from the southernmost parts of the Sahara Desert, down to the equatorial forests and almost into South Africa. Today they live in a few remaining isolated pockets, forced there by the threat of poaching. In response to the ivory trade and illegal hunting of elephants, a pile of tusks was burnt publicly in Kenya, in 1989.

W E ARE more aware than ever of the variety of ways in which human activity threatens certain animal species. For millions of years animals have been hunted all over the world for food and clothing. Overhunting has led to a drastic reduction in the numbers of species world-wide, including the rhinos of Africa and the narwhals of the Arctic. Only about a hundred golden lion tamarins still exist since large parts of their rainforest habitat have been burnt down and many of the tamarins have been captured to sell as pets or to zoos. The destruction of wild-life habitats for farming, industry, housing and transport has also played a major role in bringing animals close to extinction.

Barn owls have rapidly decreased in number because of a reduction in the extent of their habitat. The kakapo, a New

The darker green on the map shows the African elephant range in 1900. Red shows its present range.

Animal challenge
As humans alter the environment, animals gradually change to adapt to the new conditions. Some build up a resistance to poisonous substances, others learn to eat different foods, while a few simply develop an ability to run quickly, or use new skills to avoid being killed. Some adapt very successfully, but

Tasmanian tiger
A relative of the kangaroo and once common in Tasmania, this tiger is now extinct. Many died from disease while others were killed by hunters until, in 1936, the last known Tasmanian tiger died in a zoo.

others cannot cope with the new conditions and species may die out, that is, become extinct. In order to save endangered species, therefore, it is necessary to create conditions they can cope with.

Animals at risk

A few of the many animal species in danger of extinction are shown below:
1. Golden lion tamarin.
2. Kakapo
3. White rhino
4. Barn owl
5. Mountain lion
6. Malayan tapir
7. Narwhal

Zealand parrot, is threatened by the grazing of deer which damages its habitat by destroying or damaging vegetation. The kakapo is unique because, unlike other parrots, it cannot fly. The mountain lion, or cougar, of North America has become rare because of extensive hunting in the past. Another endangered animal, now rarely sighted, is the Malayan tapir which lives in the rainforests of Southeast Asia.

It is not only on land that animal species are driven close to extinction. Around 30,000 sperm whales were hunted and killed a year at one time; now they are only seen in small groups of about 10. The Mediterranean monk seal was once common throughout the Mediterranean and Black Seas and in the Atlantic coastal waters off North Africa. But now there are fewer than 500 in existence. Although the monk seal is now legally protected from hunting, it still suffers from the of tourism along Mediterranean coasts.

Blue whale

The blue whale can live in all oceanic areas of the world. It is the largest animal in the world, weighing as much as 30 elephants and growing to 30 metres in length. At birth, baby blue whales are 7 tonnes in weight. Whalers search for and kill many blue whales every year, and so many have been killed this century they are now very rare. In the waters of the Antarctic, for example, there were approximately 220,000 blue whales at the beginning of the century. Today the same waters are home to fewer than 1,000.

Dangers of dumping

The beautiful white polar bear lives in the cold Arctic regions. Until recently the bears have survived the onslaught of human activity, but with the encroachment of humans into their habitats serious problems are being created for these inquisitive creatures. Pollution and the dumping of waste can easily lead to injury and disease in animals.

Some of the world's greatest rivers rise in the Himalayas. The Yangtze and the Yellow River flow north-eastward through China, the Ganges and the Brahmaputra reach the sea at Calcutta to the south. The Himalayas also have many glaciers which melt rapidly during the spring, sending torrents of water down the mountain sides. The huge rivers erode the steep mountain slopes and carry the broken rock to the sea, breaking it into smaller and smaller particles as it travels. As the sea slows the river down, the now tiny particles settle to form a delta, such as the Ganges Delta in Calcutta.

Himalayas

THE collision between the Indian and Eurasian plates occurred between 40 and 60 million years ago. It created the world's largest mountain chain, the Himalayas, which stretches for over 12,000 kilometres.

The section of crust we know as India forced its way 3000 kilometres into the Eurasian crust. The force was immense, lifting, splitting and folding rock that before had been below the sea which covered the region. India is

Floods

Bangladesh is mainly situated on the low-lying delta of the Ganges River. The area is densely populated and the flooding which sweeps across the region takes the lives of thousands of people. The floods are due to heavy rain falling inland during the monsoon, which causes the river to overflow. Storm surges from the Bay of Bengal also create devastating floods, with giant wind-driven waves crashing over the delta.

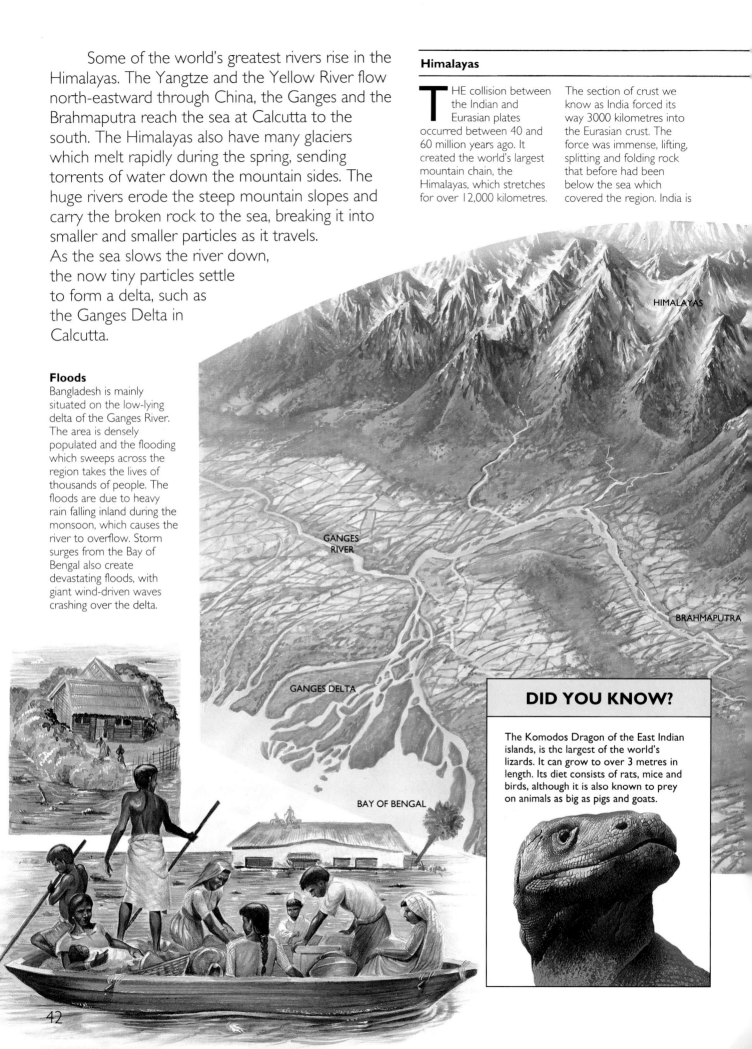

HIMALAYAS

GANGES RIVER

BRAHMAPUTRA

GANGES DELTA

BAY OF BENGAL

DID YOU KNOW?

The Komodos Dragon of the East Indian islands, is the largest of the world's lizards. It can grow to over 3 metres in length. Its diet consists of rats, mice and birds, although it is also known to prey on animals as big as pigs and goats.

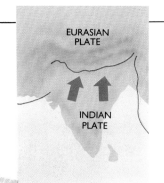

EURASIAN PLATE

INDIAN PLATE

now continuing to collide into Eurasia, but at a slower rate, causing earthquakes. These earthquakes threaten the whole Himalayan region, setting off destructive landslides which carry vast quantities of soil down the steep mountain slopes to the rivers below.

The farthest extreme of Southeast Asia is made up of several chains of volcanic islands, formed where the Indian, Pacific and Eurasian plates collide. Some of these islands, such as the Philippines, are part of the `Great Pacific Ring of Fire': a line of volcanic and tectonic activity around the edge of the Pacific Ocean, where different plates meet. Java alone has 150 volcanoes, of which 50 are active. The volcanic island of Krakatau, which lies between Sumatra and Java, has seen a succession of eruptions.

Mount Everest

Mount Everest is at the eastern end of the Himalayas and is the highest mountain in the world, soaring above the clouds to a height of 8848 metres. Its summit has long been the goal of climbers. In 1953 the famous explorer, Sir Edmund Hillary and Tenzing Norgay were the first to reach its summit. After many other dangerous expeditions by mountaineers, Reinhold Messner was the first to reach the summit alone in 1980, without the help of a radio or oxygen tank.

A fiery past

The 3000-kilometre long chain of volcanic islands which make up Indonesia occurs at the boundary between the Indian, Eurasian and Pacific plates. One island, Krakatau, has risen from the sea, collapsed and reformed several times throughout its history. The island we see today is around 200 metres above sea level, last rising from the sea in a volcanic explosion in 1927.

KRAKATAU AD416   1883   1985

Mount Fuji

The highest peak in Japan, Mount Fuji erupted for the first time 10,000 years ago. Buried beneath its surface are the remnants of two previous volcanoes, Komi-Take, formed 300,000 years ago, and Old Fuji, which appeared 60,000 years ago. The new Mount Fuji has erupted a total of ten times since AD800, the last time being in 1707, but it now lies silent. Through the years the austere mountain has been worshipped by the Japanese people.

China's Sorrow

THE Yellow River, or Huang Ho, of China runs for 4000 kilometres, from its source in the Himalayas to its mouth at the Gulf of Chihli. It carries the most suspended sediment of any river in the world, transporting 16 billion tonnes to the sea every year. The river's burden comes from two sources: first, the river flows through an area of easily eroded material called loess, which

Northern and eastern Asia covers a vast region. In the far north are the frozen arctic lands of northern Siberia. South of these frozen regions is the tundra, stretching in a band from west to east. Here the ground is frozen for much of the year, with only some gentle melting of the surface during the short summer season. Days are very short in the winter and very long in the summer. South of the tundra is a band of coniferous forest, and south of this on the east coast an area of deciduous woodland. Inland in Asia there is a large area of grassland called the steppe where drier conditions are found.

Guilin mountains

The beautiful Guilin mountains in southern China show the powerful effect water can have on a landscape of limestone rock. Carbonate in limestone is easily dissolved by acidic rainwater. Joints and bedding planes provide passageways through the rock, allowing water to percolate and dissolve the rock from within. The joints are enlarged to form swallow holes, reaching deep into the rock. Huge underground caves form and eventually their roofs collapse to leave steep-sided gorges, separated by towering mountains. In this way, the Guilin region was changed from a flat landscape into a mountain scene that has inspired artists for many years.

44

it picks up and carries. Secondly, because the rainfall is not high enough for dense vegetation to grow on surrounding slopes, rainstorms easily erode the ground, sending extra sediment down to the river.

The Yellow River is called 'China's Sorrow' because of its devastating floods. In 1931, the river broke its banks, killing over 3 million people. The river-bed is continuously rising as silt settles on the bottom. As it crosses the Yellow Plain, the river is around 7 metres above the sur-rounding fields, and dykes have been constructed to keep the river in place. The river constantly changes position and can migrate up to 300 metres a day. The maps show how the river's course has changed dramatically over the years.

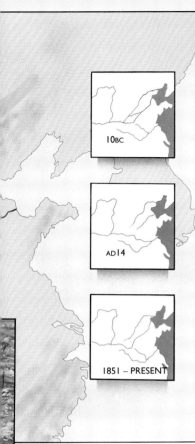

10BC

AD14

1851 – PRESENT

Shilin karst

Some of the most attractive karst scenery to be found in China is that around Shilin, in Yunnan Province. Water has dissolved the rock to form a mass of sharp-topped towers, ranging from 5 to 30 metres high. Known as the Forest of Stones, it is a maze of limestone pillars, ravines, trees and deep pools of water. The limestone rocks resemble certain lifelike images and some have been given imaginative names, such as 'Phoenix Preening its Feathers'.

A few survivors

There are fewer than a thousand giant pandas surviving in the bamboo forests of south-west China. Bamboo is their main diet but in the face of com-petition from humans, their natural habitat and food source has been under threat for many years. Bamboo is one of the most useful plants in the world. The Chinese have used bamboo for over 2000 years, making fishing rods, furniture and even scaffolding as certain types are stronger than steel.

DID YOU KNOW?

The clever Japanese macaques have learnt to escape the cold of winter by sitting up to their necks in the warm water of volcanic springs. Unfortunately though, when it snows their heads become covered in several centimetres of snow.

A hot spring in Beppau, Japan, is named the Bloody Pond of Hell because of its bright red colour. The colour comes from iron oxide dissolved in the water.

The heart of central Asia is desert. The famous Gobi Desert in China is part of this vast Asian desert. The Yellow River flows across its southern edge, gushing from the heights of the Himalayan mountains. These spectacular mountains rise dramatically at the southern end of the desert, with many of their peaks attaining heights of 6000 metres. The Tibetan Plateau lies to the north of the Himalayas and is over 4800 metres above sea level. On the southern side of the Himalayas the land level drops again, the climate becomes warmer and wetter and the vegetation changes to grassland, and finally to rainforest near the equator.

OCEANIA

THE continent of Oceania (Australasia) is composed of thousands of small islands in the Pacific Ocean, New Zealand and the large landmass of Australia. This continent is the smallest and the lowest of all the continents, being just 300 metres high on average. Apart from Antarctica, it is also the driest. The landmass of Australia contains 150,000 square kilometres of desert (20 per cent of its area), including the Great Sandy Desert and the Gibson Desert.

The eastern edge of Australia is a long, thin coastal strip running from north to south. On moving in from the coast, the land begins to rise steeply near the Great Divide, a long chain of mountains. Further west the land level drops gradually onto an endless expanse of low, flat plains, under 200 metres high. Mountains formed 3000 million years ago were eroded to create these plateaux which now cover 75 per cent of Australia's surface.

1. The island of Papua New Guinea houses many bizarre creatures and beautiful flowers. The world's largest moth is found here and there are several thousand species of orchid.

NEW GUINEA

BARKLY TABLELAND

Diamantina

KIMBERLEY PLATEAU

MACDONNELL RANGES

L. Eyre

②

AYERS ROCK

L. Torrens

MUSGRAVE RANGES

L. Gairdner

GREAT SANDY DESERT

GIBSON DESERT

INDIAN OCEAN

GREAT AUSTRALIAN BIGHT

GREAT VICTORIA DESERT

Ashburton

Gascoyne

NULLARBOR PLAIN

Bora Bora

The islands of Polynesia are found in the south of the Pacific Ocean, many thousands of kilometres from any continent. They are volcanic islands, having risen from the sea in spectacular eruptions. Many are surrounded by beautiful coral reefs, called fringing and barrier reefs. The island of Bora Bora is found in the chain of Polynesian islands called the Society Islands. It has a central volcanic cone, and is separated from an impressive reef by a shallow lagoon.

PACIFIC OCEAN

CORAL SEA

GREAT BARRIER REEF

GREAT DIVIDING RANGE

SELWYN RANGE

MURRAY-DARLING DRAINAGE BASIN

AUSTRALIAN ALPS

Murray

TASMANIA

TASMAN SEA

2. Lake Eyre is the largest in Oceania. When flooded it covers 8900 square kilometres, but for most of the year it is a dry basin, much of the water having evaporated in the heat.

3. New Zealand is very remote. It has evolved its own plant species which are found nowhere else, such as tree ferns growing to 15 metres.

4. Mount Cook on the South Island of New Zealand is the highest mountain in Oceania, at 3764 metres.

Geysers of New Zealand

Geysers are named from an Icelandic word meaning to 'gush forth'. Water is heated to boiling point by rocks below ground, causing it to shoot into the air in spouts hundreds of metres high. Geysers are found wherever water can penetrate into the geothermal heat source, up to 5 kilometres below ground. In New Zealand there are many geysers, including a record-setting geyser which shot 450 metres in the air, and flung a boulder weighing 150 pounds over half a kilometre away.

③

NEW ZEALAND

④

Duck-billed platypus
Found in eastern Australia and Tasmania, the duck-billed platypus is one of the strangest animals in the world. It has webbed feet and a 'beak' like a duck, and it even lays eggs. But it also spends a lot of time underwater, and has fur and a flat tail like a beaver. It lives in burrows on the banks of rivers and streams.

Australia has been separated from other continents for so long its animals have evolved into unusual types. Of the world's 16 families of marsupials, 13 are found only in Australia. Marsupials, such as the kangaroo and koala, care for their very young by providing a protective pouch for them to live in. Their offspring are born before they are fully developed and survive in the pouch, instead of remaining in the womb until fully formed. The wild dogs, or dingos, were probably brought

Usually we think of a desert as a barren expanse of dust, sand or rock. But after rainfall the deserts of Australia can become carpeted with flowers. Huge numbers of desert flowers will all bloom together, making the most of the rare water supply.

to Australia about 8000 years ago as domestic dogs. Since then they have become wild again. The flightless emu, which looks similar to an ostrich, has been in Australia for about 80 million years. Like the ostriches of Africa, the emu can escape from danger by running at speeds of up to 50 kilometres per hour.

A red giant

FROM a vast, flat plain in the Uluru National Park, a solitary mountain rises steeply above the horizon. A solid block of sandstone, Ayers Rock reaches a height of 348 metres and has a length of about 3 kilometres.

Around 500 million years ago the huge rock was part of an ocean floor which stretched across central Australia. The rock has since survived movements in the Earth's crust and millions of years of erosion. Horizontal layers in the rock have been upturned and, like an iceberg, the bulk of the rock now lies out of sight. It has been estimated that the rock reaches a depth of 6 kilometres below ground level.

Iron ore gives Ayers Rock its colour which, predominantly red, can appear to change at dawn and dusk. Weathering has

Bungle Bungle Range
The Bungle Bungle Range of mountains are eroded domes of 370-million-year-old sandstone. The labyrinth of mountain tops lie in a remote region of western Australia.

48

carved caves, ridges and grooves into the surface of the sandstone. Many such intricate features have been named: a depression of ridges and grooves is known as the Brain; a strip of rock left standing above crumbling sandstone is called the Kangaroo's Tail.

Ayers Rock is sacred to Aborigines. Local tribes call it Uluru, which means 'great pebble' and tourists are forbidden to enter many of their caves.

Threat to rainforest

When a new dam and lakes were proposed in Tasmania, protesters came from all over the world. The lakes would flood one of the only three temperate rainforests left in the world. After strong criticism from conservationists, the plan was dropped.

DID YOU KNOW?

Containing as much as ten tonnes of mud, a termite mound can stand three or four times higher than a human being. Several millions of the tiny insects live inside.

The cliffs of the Great Australian Bight are the longest line of unbroken cliffs in the world. They stretch for about 200 kilometres.

In the Nambung National Park thousands of limestone pillars rise like ruins from the barren plain. They developed as limestone formed around the roots of trees and plants.

Boab tree

The boab tree of Australia is closely related to the baobab trees of Africa and Madagascar. It is possible that the baobab fruit was carried across the sea on flotsam to Australia. On Australia's north-west coast it may have taken root, where they can be found growing today.

The trunk of the boab grows to more than 9 metres thick and is one of the largest trees known.

AFRICA

THE African continent is the second largest after Asia. It has a broad equatorial zone, with an interior of tropical forest. Largely inaccessible to travellers, forest life thrives in the high humidity and temperatures of the region. Moving to the north or south of the equatorial zone, conditions become much drier and the savanna zone, a dry, extensive grassland, is found. Further north, conditions become dry enough for there to be a desert: the Sahara Desert, the largest in the world. In the south, a similar pattern can be traced, from rainforest, to savanna, to desert, ending in Namibia, with the Kalahari Desert.

The African continent has several huge rivers. The Congo river basin contains a myriad of rivers and, covering almost 4 million square kilometres, is second in size only to the Amazon river basin in South America. The River Nile is the longest river in the world. Its total length is 6695 kilometres. At the Sudanese border with Egypt, the Nile is dammed by a huge structure called the Aswan Dam, designed to control the flow of the vast river and to provide hydroelectric power.

1. The Sahara has not been desert. From 5000-2000 BC, as rock paintings in the Tassili highland shelters show, cattle were grazed on the surrounding grasslands.

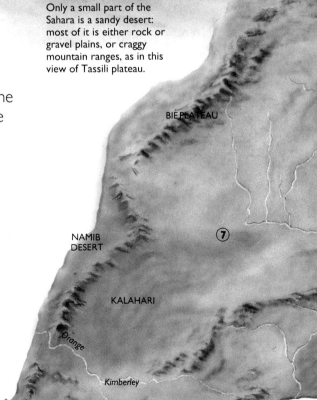

Only a small part of the Sahara is a sandy desert: most of it is either rock or gravel plains, or craggy mountain ranges, as in this view of Tassili plateau.

2. The banks of the River Nile, flooded every summer, are heavily cultivated. As in the past, when Egypt was one of the first great civilizations, millions of people depend on the waters of the Nile.
3. In the dry grasslands away from the waters of the Niger, many Sahel peoples struggle to carry on their centuries-old existence.
4. The East African Rift valley, a long split between two plates in the Earth's crust,

extends from the mouth of the Zambezi to the Red Sea.
5. Kilimanjaro (Swahili for 'Great Mountain') is Africa's highest peak.
6. The Ngorongoro Crater is all that is left of a huge, exploded volano. It is now a wildlife reserve.
7. Every June or July, the Okavango River floods its delta, an area of inland drainage in the desert of northern Botswana. As a result, there is abundant plant and animal life.

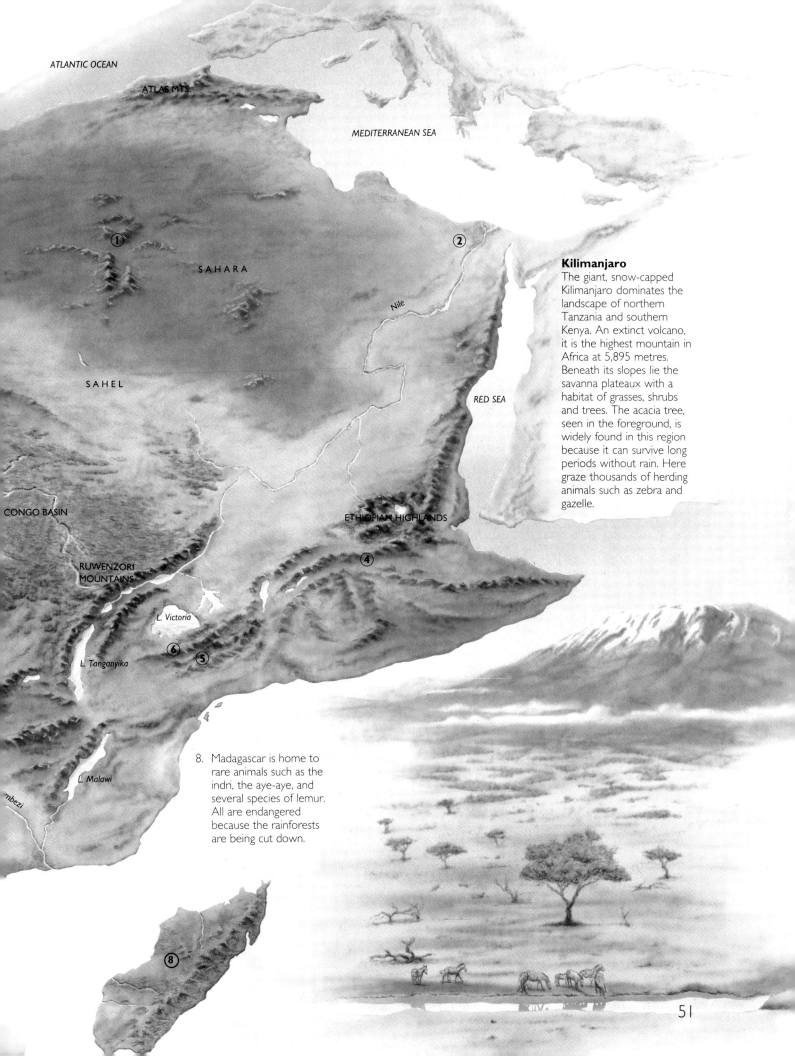

ATLANTIC OCEAN

ATLAS MTS.

MEDITERRANEAN SEA

① SAHARA

②

Nile

SAHEL

RED SEA

CONGO BASIN

ETHIOPIAN HIGHLANDS

④

RUWENZORI
MOUNTAINS

L. Victoria

⑥ ⑤

L. Tanganyika

L. Malawi

mbezi

8. Madagascar is home to
rare animals such as the
indri, the aye-aye, and
several species of lemur.
All are endangered
because the rainforests
are being cut down.

⑧

Kilimanjaro
The giant, snow-capped
Kilimanjaro dominates the
landscape of northern
Tanzania and southern
Kenya. An extinct volcano,
it is the highest mountain in
Africa at 5,895 metres.
Beneath its slopes lie the
savanna plateaux with a
habitat of grasses, shrubs
and trees. The acacia tree,
seen in the foreground, is
widely found in this region
because it can survive long
periods without rain. Here
graze thousands of herding
animals such as zebra and
gazelle.

In the past, Africa was joined to Arabia and the Red Sea did not exist. Plate movement over the last 30 million years created the Red Sea, as Africa and Arabia moved further apart. The tearing of the land opened up the narrow Rift Valley which runs southwards from northern Arabia, through eastern Africa. Continued movement in the future will widen the Rift Valley, allowing the eastern part of Africa to drift free from the main continent, like the island of Madagascar.

Desert landscapes

IN THE centre of the Sahara, where less than one centimetre of rain falls per year, the Hoggar Massif rises from a rocky plain. It is made up of basalt columns which are the source of much of the sand found in other parts of the desert. They break down into fine sand particles which are blown together to form rippled dunes. Huge sand dunes move bodily across the desert, sometimes shaped as crescents (called barchan dunes) but often shaped as straight lines (called seif dunes). Strange shaped rocks form when a hard crusted top layer of rock remains protected, while the lower rock is eroded by the abrasive, sandy winds.

East Africa's Rift
The Great Rift Valley of East Africa is a huge chasm in the Earth's surface. The surrounding landscape is dominated by deep valleys, tall, steep mountains and hundreds of lakes. Here one also finds such craters as the Ngorongoro Crater, a sheltered haven for wildlife which was formed over 3 million years ago in a great volcanic explosion.

Along the Rift Valley the plates of Africa and Somali are ripping apart, opening up a great crack in the Earth's surface, allowing molten lava to surge to the surface and build towering volcanoes. This slow but dramatic movement is accompanied by the faulting and crumpling of the surrounding rock to form high mountain ranges.

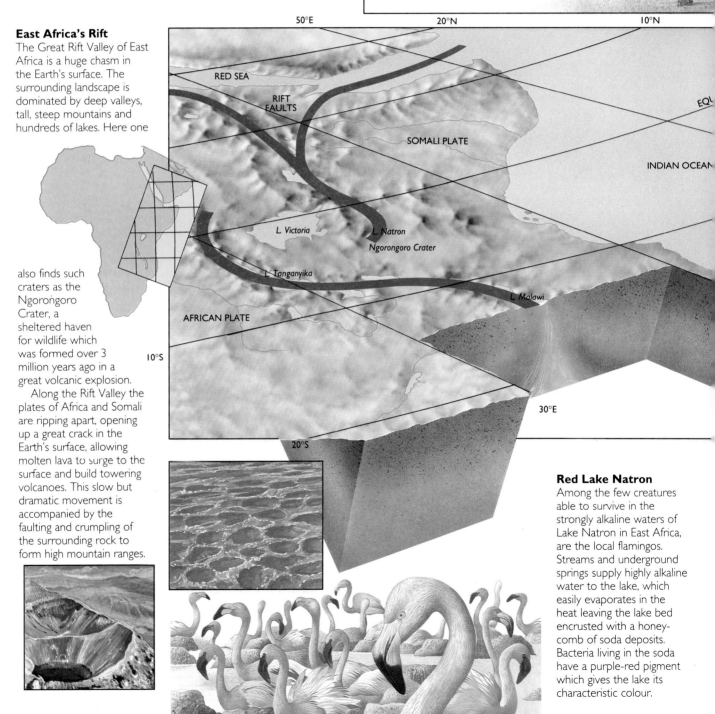

Red Lake Natron
Among the few creatures able to survive in the strongly alkaline waters of Lake Natron in East Africa, are the local flamingos. Streams and underground springs supply highly alkaline water to the lake, which easily evaporates in the heat leaving the lake bed encrusted with a honeycomb of soda deposits. Bacteria living in the soda have a purple-red pigment which gives the lake its characteristic colour.

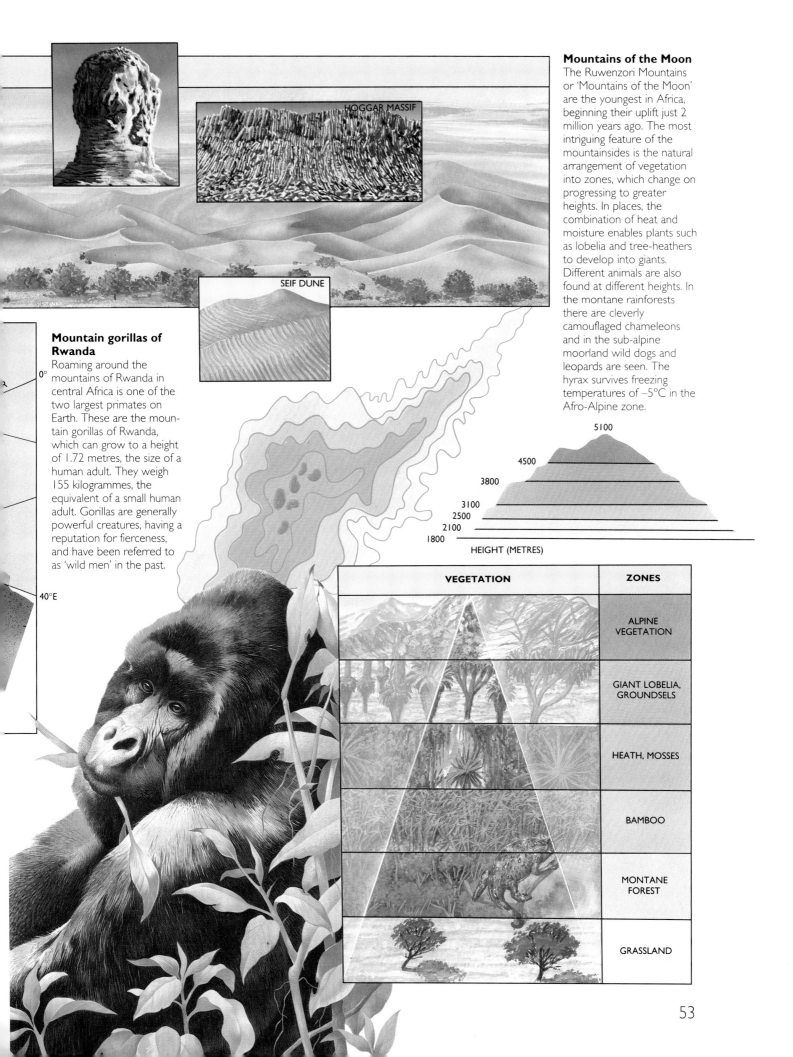

HOGGAR MASSIF

SEIF DUNE

Mountains of the Moon

The Ruwenzori Mountains or 'Mountains of the Moon' are the youngest in Africa, beginning their uplift just 2 million years ago. The most intriguing feature of the mountainsides is the natural arrangement of vegetation into zones, which change on progressing to greater heights. In places, the combination of heat and moisture enables plants such as lobelia and tree-heathers to develop into giants. Different animals are also found at different heights. In the montane rainforests there are cleverly camouflaged chameleons and in the sub-alpine moorland wild dogs and leopards are seen. The hyrax survives freezing temperatures of –5°C in the Afro-Alpine zone.

Mountain gorillas of Rwanda

Roaming around the mountains of Rwanda in central Africa is one of the two largest primates on Earth. These are the mountain gorillas of Rwanda, which can grow to a height of 1.72 metres, the size of a human adult. They weigh 155 kilogrammes, the equivalent of a small human adult. Gorillas are generally powerful creatures, having a reputation for fierceness, and have been referred to as 'wild men' in the past.

0°

40°E

5100
4500
3800
3100
2500
2100
1800

HEIGHT (METRES)

VEGETATION	ZONES
	ALPINE VEGETATION
	GIANT LOBELIA, GROUNDSELS
	HEATH, MOSSES
	BAMBOO
	MONTANE FOREST
	GRASSLAND

AYE-AYE

Okavango Delta

The Okavango River flows south-east through Namibia from the Angolan Highlands and into Botswana. Seasonal flooding causes sediment to spread into an alluvial fan to form the Okavango Delta – the world's largest inland delta. In March and April flood waters double the area of swamp and, in June and July, hundreds of animals and birds make their way to the delta in search of water and food. They are driven up from the Kalahari Desert by the harsh climate. The largest concentration of African elephants is found at the waterside, with up to 60,000 in a herd. Some of the other animals that seek refuge here are leopards, buffalo and antelopes, as well as giraffe, crocodiles and the greatest killer of African people in the animal kingdom, the hippopotamus. The papyrus that surrounds the swamp is alive with smaller creatures, including insects, frogs and fish.

Okavango

SWAMP AREA
AFTER FLOOD

The southern half of the African continent contains desert, grassland and rainforest. The Kalahari Desert contains animals and plants with clever adaptions so that they can survive in the arid conditions. Many animals shelter below ground during the day to avoid the midday sun. The Kalahari ground squirrel can survive by carrying its bushy tail above its body, keeping itself completely in the shade.

54

Madagascar

MADAGASCAR is the fourth largest island in the world. It separated from the African mainland about 100 million years ago and now lies off the south-east coast of Africa. The island's isolated animals evolved separately to become unique, and of all Madagascar's animals 95 per cent are found nowhere else in the world. Lemurs, such as the ring-tailed lemur, are only found in Madagascar, along with the lemur's relative, the rare aye-aye, and the radiated tortoise, one of the island's many endangered species. The natural habitats of various animals are in danger. For example, human activity threatens the survival of animals living in a thin strip of rainforest along the eastern coast.

RADIATED TORTOISE

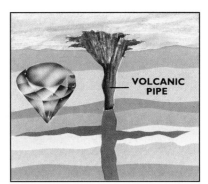

VOLCANIC PIPE

Diamonds
In 1905 the world's largest diamond was discovered in South Africa. It was the size of a person's fist. Diamonds are found in volcanic pipe-like structures known as kimberlites, first found at Kimberley in South Africa.

All the wilderness area of Africa used to be filled with animals but due to growing cities, expanding farms and hunting, the number of animals has been greatly reduced. In the grassland region the Serengeti National Park protects a spectacular variety of wildlife in an area of around 13,000 square kilometres. Animals include zebras, lions, warthogs, hyenas and wildebeests. Giraffes, the tallest land animals, are also found feeding off the acacia trees that grow on the grassy plains.

Victoria Falls
The Victoria Falls are one of the most spectacular views in the African continent. Plunging into a gorge below, the falls can send mists of water rising over 900 metres into the air. Located on the Zambezi River, the falls produce the world's largest curtain of falling water, over 2 kilometres from bank to bank and over 120 metres high. The gorge below zig-zags back and forth, following the pattern of joints and fractures in the basaltic rock. Since the middle of the Pleistocene period the falls have retreated 8 kilometres by wearing back the rock.

DID YOU KNOW?

In south-west Africa a forest of trees appears to grow upside-down, with their 'roots' poking out of the ground.

Lungfish have air-breathing lungs and can survive dry seasons by burrowing into the mud.

The welwitschia plant grows in arid regions of Namibia, gathering moisture from fog. Some are 2000 years old.

Table Mountain
Overlooking Cape Town in South Africa is a giant steep-sided, flat-topped hill. Table Mountain, as it is called, is a huge mesa, capped by hard sandstone which prevents it from being eroded as rapidly as the surrounding lowlands. Clouds spilling over the edge of the table-shaped mountain are said to look like a large white tablecloth coating the rock.

ANTARCTICA

T HE Antarctic continent is the coldest, bleakest place on Earth. At night the temperature can fall as low as −52°C, and regular gusts of 320 kilometre per hour winds sweep across the surface. Much of the land is covered by an immense ice sheet, 4000 metres thick. On average, it is 1.5°C colder in the Antarctic than in the Arctic. This is because the Arctic receives more heat from warmer areas to the south, brought by ocean currents.

The Antarctic has not always been as cold as it is today. A temperate climate and lush, dense vegetation were typical of the Antarctic 150 million years ago because at that time the land lay much closer to the equator. Since then, the Antarctic plate carrying the landmass of Antarctica has drifted southwards to occupy its current position over the South Pole, and has acquired its cold, windy climate. The only plants that grow there now are mosses, fungi and lichens, and just three species of flowering plants.

1. Beneath the ice there is just a 965 kilometre stretch of land connecting the Ross Sea and Weddell Sea.
2. Mount Erebus on the edge of the Ross Ice Shelf is the only active volcano in Antarctica.
3. The Ross Sea extends further south than any other part of the world's oceans. Its southern limit is only 450 kilometres from the South Pole. However, near the South Pole, most of the sea is under the Ross Ice Shelf.
4. At the South Pole there are six months of daylight and six months of darkness as the Earth orbits the Sun every year. The race to be first at the South Pole was

won by Roald Amundsen in December 1911. The British explorer Robert Falcon Scott finally reached the Pole in January 1912, only to find that Amundsen had already been there.
5. At Vostok the lowest temperature on Earth was recorded: −89°C.

The large white rafts of ice that float across the Arctic and Antarctic waters are called icebergs. They form by breaking off or 'calving' from a land-based glacier where it reaches the sea, or from the edge of an ice shelf. An ice shelf is a vast plain of ice floating on the sea, sometimes as an extension of a land-based ice sheet.

SOUTH ATLANTIC OCEAN

WEDDELL SEA

RONNE ICE SHELF

VINSON MASSIF

①

SOUTH POLE
④

AMUNDSEN SEA

TRANSANTARCTIC MOUNTAINS

ROSS ICE SHELF

SOUTH PACIFIC OCEAN

ROSS SEA

② DRY VALLEYS

③

56

Icebergs

Icebergs can be of many different sizes. Thin flat ice masses are called ice floes, while smaller icebergs below 10 metres in diameter, are referred to as ice cakes. The largest icebergs which form can create their own climate by interfering with air circulation, and are also a fearsome hazard for ships.

Icebergs of the Antarctic differ from those of the Arctic waters. In the northern Arctic waters, floating ice masses appear to be more ragged and angular in form, whereas in the southern Antarctic waters they are more evenly shaped.

The ice we see floating on the water is only 10 per cent of the iceberg. The remaining 90 per cent is beneath the water, being carried along by currents.

ANTARCTIC OCEAN

INDIAN OCEAN

PRINCE CHARLES MOUNTAINS

AMERY ICE SHELF

SHACKLETON ICE SHELF

⑤

Humpbacked whale

THERE is an abundance of zooplankton such as krill in the waters of the Antarctic Ocean, upon which the grey humpbacked whale flourishes. The whale has a clever system of feeding on the krill. It creates a net of bubbles surrounding the krill and then trails through the centre sucking in tens of thousands of the tiny fish in great mouthfuls.

Wright Valley

In parts of the Antarctic where ice sheets do not cover the land, there are steep mountains separated by long dry valleys. There are three major dry valleys in the Antarctic: the Wright, Victoria and Taylor. Each extends for over 40 kilometres and is up to 5 kilometres wide. The air is so cold not even snow can form, and there is very little life. The valley can only be eroded by wind carrying rocky fragments which blasts the valley rocks to form bizarre shapes.

WRIGHT VALLEY

Antarctic waste

As with all natural habitats, it is important to protect the wildlife and environment of the world's ice-covered regions. As they become more accessible the danger of destruction by humans increases. Waste products are dumped on the pack ice or at sea where they pollute and destroy marine life.

Although the Antarctic Ocean is cold, the sea-bed provides a stable environment for diverse communities of marine plants and animals. Unlike the oceans, the land provides a very unstable environment for Antarctic wildlife. Islands appear and disappear due to the movement of the Earth's crust, and ice advances and retreats every year. There are relatively few bird species in the region, although albatrosses and penguins are seen in huge colonies on Antarctic shores.

Penguins are flightless birds. The largest is the giant emperor penguin, which can live for over 20 years. Although penguins move slowly and are clumsy on land, they are agile swimmers and can cover great distances in search of fish to eat. They tend to live in large colonies of up to a million penguins.

Ozone hole

IN THE atmosphere above the Antarctic continent an ozone hole seems to be getting steadily bigger. The hole is of increasing concern, because the ozone layer provides protection from the harmful ultraviolet rays of the Sun. The ozone is being slowly destroyed by chlorofluorocarbons (CFCs) in the atmosphere, which come from aerosols and refrigerator coolants.

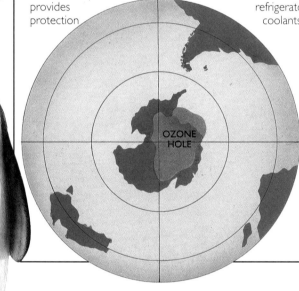

OZONE HOLE

Beneath the ice

If the thick Antarctic ice cover were to be stripped away, a dramatic landscape would emerge. Mountain ranges, high above sea level, would be uncovered. In places they already poke out above the ice surface, such as at the Vinson Massif, which rises 5140 metres above sea level. In other places the land surface would be forced to drop well below the sea level, having been depressed by the great weight of overlying ice.

DID YOU KNOW?

Features such as glaciers, ice sheets and icebergs often contain coloured stripes, caused by different layers of ice which have accumulated every year.

Weddell seals can stay underwater for over an hour; they surface at breathing holes cut in the ice.

BREATHING HOLE

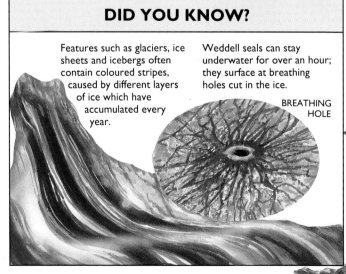

A CHANGING CLIMATE

Ocean currents

The coast of north-west Europe is ice-free in winter, but at the same latitude in eastern Canada and the United States, the coast is packed with thick ice every year. The Gulf Stream ocean current brings warm water up from the Caribbean, preventing the formation of sea ice and affecting the climate of north-west Europe. If the supply of warm water was cut off or changed its direction, the climate would alter significantly.

THE Earth's climate has seen many changes. In the past there have been ice ages and today there is evidence of global warming, but scientists are still unsure about the causes. One explanation is that the Earth has changed its position relative to the Sun. Another idea is that as the continental land masses have drifted around, the circulation of ocean currents has been interrupted, affecting global climatic patterns. There are also ideas relating to changes in the radiation emitted by the Sun. However, the most recent ideas emphasize the importance of greenhouse gases, such as carbon dioxide and methane. These gases occur naturally but human activities are causing their increase *(see below)*.

Dinosaur death

Climatic change may have had a role in the widespread and rapid extinction of the world's dinosaurs. The change was thought to have been caused by an asteroid hitting the Earth. Dust and particles thrown into the atmosphere would have blocked solar radiation, causing climatic cooling, and creating an environment in which dinosaurs could no longer live.

Global greenhouse

Greenhouse gases let short-wave radiation pass through on its way from the Sun. The Earth absorbs this radiation, warms and re-radiates it as long-wave radiation. The greenhouse gases trap this heat and send it back to Earth, making the atmosphere warmer.

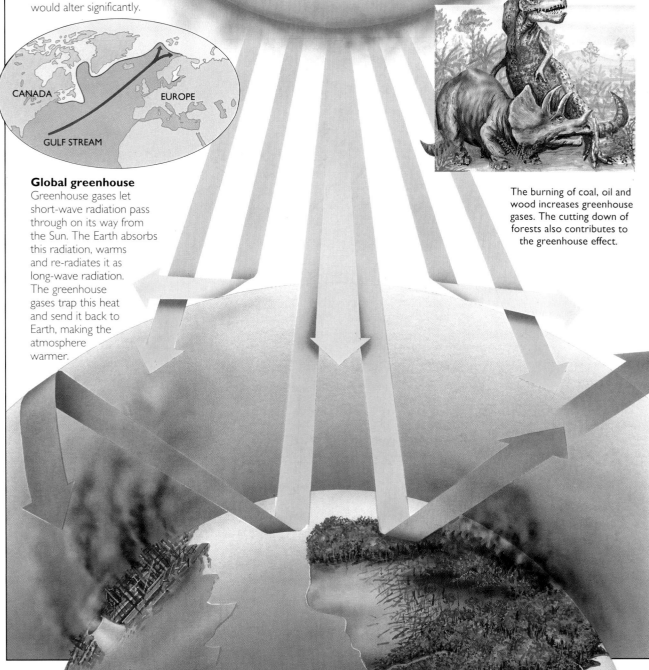

The burning of coal, oil and wood increases greenhouse gases. The cutting down of forests also contributes to the greenhouse effect.

CANADA

EUROPE

GULF STREAM

GLOSSARY

Aridity	A lack of moisture, usually occurring where evaporation is greater than precipitation.
Atmosphere	The envelope of gases that surrounds the Earth.
Biome	A community of animals and plants living in a particular environment which covers a large area.
Calcite	A deposit of calcium carbonate, sometimes called tufa.
Carboniferous Period	The period of time 345 to 280 million years ago, during which Carboniferous rocks were deposited.
Coniferous	A group of trees which bears cones, such as pines, yews and firs.
Convection currents	Currents driven by heat differences. They occur in the atmosphere where the air near the ground is warmer than above and also in the mantle of the Earth.
Deciduous	Trees which shed their leaves in winter, such as beech, oak and chestnut.
Delta	The accumulation of sediment brought by rivers and deposited. Deltas usually occur at the coast, but can also form inland.
Deposition	A process in which sediment that can no longer be carried by ice, water or wind is left on the land or sea-bed.
Desert	An area receiving less than 25 centimetres of rainfall a year. It can be in regions that are hot or cold.
Earthquakes	Vibrations or tremors in the Earth's crust which can be felt without the aid of instruments.
Ecology	The scientific study of the relationships between plants, animals and their environment.
Ecosystem	A complex system of interacting plants and animals, and the environment in which they live.
Epiphyte	A plant which grows on another plant, using it for support but not for nutrition. They are especially common in rainforests.
Equator	An imaginary circle around the Earth, dividing it into two hemispheres.
Erosion	The break-up and removal of rocks by water, wind and ice.
Evaporation	The process by which water is changed from its liquid to its gaseous form through heating.
Extinction	The process whereby certain species of animal and plant cease to exist on Earth.
Food web	A series of organisms with related feeding habits. Some of the organisms are the food supply of others in the web.
Fossil	A remnant or trace of a former living thing preserved in rock.
Glacier	A moving mass of ice formed by snow accumulation, usually occupying a valley.
Humidity	The amount of water vapour contained in the atmosphere.
Ice age	A period of global cooling when ice sheets and glaciers expand.
Igneous	A type of rock formed when molten magma solidifies.
Lava	Molten magma from inside the Earth which has escaped to the surface through volcanic activity.
Limestone	A sedimentary rock composed mainly of calcium carbonate and usually containing joints and bedding planes. Limestone is also a permeable rock.
Magma	Molten rock deep within the Earth; it is usually semi-fluid.

Mangrove	A type of tree that grows in coastal regions which are normally flooded with sea water at high tide.
Metamorphic rock	A type of rock which forms after being subjected to intense heat and pressure.
Molecules	Combinations of atoms forming chemically distinct substances.
Monsoon	Seasons in which rain-bearing winds flow overland from the sea, usually producing exceptionally large rainstorms.
Ocean currents	Large bodies of moving water, their flow being due to heat differences in the water.
Peninsula	A piece of land which sticks out into the sea and is almost completely surrounded by water.
Phytoplankton	Organisms in the ocean which can create food by photosynthesis.
Plates	Pieces of the Earth's crust which move around on the mantle.
Pleistocene Period	A comparatively recent period of geological time, beginning two million years ago, during which major ice advances occurred. It ended about 10,000 years ago.
Polar	Relating to the regions surrounding the North or South Poles.
Precipitation	The transfer of water from the atmosphere to the land as snow, frost, hail, dew or rain.
Rainshadow	An area sheltered from the prevailing winds and having little rainfall.
Savanna	A tropical or sub-tropical grassy plain with few trees.
Sedimentary	Rocks which have formed on the sea-bed as material has settled to the bottom.
Tectonic processes	Movements in the Earth's crust which cause mountain-building and the alteration and depression of the crust.
Temperate	A region of the world which has relatively moderate temperatures and adequate rainfall throughout the year.
Transpiration	The process whereby plants emit water vapour into the atmosphere through small pores, or stomata, in their leaves.
Tropic of Cancer	An imaginary line of latitude around the Earth at 23.5° north.
Tropic of Capricorn	An imaginary line of latitude around the Earth at 23.5° south.
Tropics	An area of the world between latitudes of 23.5° north and 23.5° south.
Tropical rainforest	Dense forest of tall trees growing in areas of high rainfall within the tropics.
Tundra	A region in high latitudes where the ground is frequently frozen, there are few plants and the length of day varies during the year.
Volcano	A hill or mountain built of ash or lava with a central crater through which molten rock escapes to the surface of the Earth.
Zooplankton	Tiny animals that live in the sea. Unlike phytoplankton, zooplankton cannot produce food through photosynthesis.

INDEX